GIANT LEAPS

Mankind's greatest scientific advances...

told by  **The Sun** and the **science museum**

Jack Challoner
Science Museum

John Perry
The Sun

Dedication

To Miki

To Laura

First published 2006 by Boxtree
an imprint of Pan Macmillan Ltd
Pan Macmillan, 20 New Wharf Road, London N1 9RR
Basingstoke and Oxford
Associated companies throughout the world
www.panmacmillan.com

ISBN-13: 978-0-7522-2624-8
ISBN-10: 0-7522-2624-X

9 8 7 6 5 4 3 2 1

A CIP catalogue record for this book is available from
the British Library.

Designed by Perfect Bound Ltd
Printed by Butler and Tanner

Written by
John Perry (The *Sun*)
and Jack Challoner (Science Museum)

Design
Dan Newman, Perfect Bound Ltd

Sun Page Design
Matthew Marsh

Cover Concept
John Perry

Picture Research
Chris Rowlin & Felicity Page

Additional Photography
Jennie Hills & Dan Newman

FOREWORD

SCIENCE can make great newspaper copy. Some of mankind's 'Giant Leaps' have changed our lives more fundamentally than any politician, artist or even war.

A handful of these stories have made front pages around the world. But more often than not scientific discoveries with extremely dramatic long-term consequences have initially received little fanfare. They have been announced quietly, after lengthy, painstaking research. Only later have the public, and newspapers, cottoned on to their importance.

This book shows you the greatest scientific and technological advances in human history as if they were front pages in Britain's best-selling daily paper, The *Sun*. Accompanying each *Sun* page is another, written and produced by experts at the Science Museum in London, which explains simply but authoritatively the hard facts behind each story.

Many of the 'stories' we have chosen happened long before the tabloid *Sun* came into being in 1969, so we have imagined how the paper would have covered them. Some occurred before the advent of the written word, before civilisation, before mankind, even – so you will have to make a Giant Leap of imagination as you read them! Many of our pages reflect the importance of a discovery with the advantage of hindsight, rather than as it was perceived at the time. We have made each *Sun* page as realistic as possible, even down to the cross-references at the end of stories. Most are only there for added authenticity, though some DO advertise a double-page *Sun* spread that follows.

The *Sun* 'splashes' are only one half of this book.

On the left-hand pages the Science Museum provides the full background to each story, setting it in the context of mankind's history and explaining its importance and its ramifications for the advancement of science, technology and the world in general.

The *Sun* pages are to entertain and the Science Museum pages to inform. If you're amused – and learn something too – we've succeeded.

John Perry
Jack Challoner

CONTENTS

You can, of course, simply read this book from front to back. But if you wish to focus on one particular aspect of science – for example, electricity, or space exploration – look out for the 'NOW JUMP TO' cross-references on each left-hand page. They will direct you, forward or back, to the other pages most relevant to the one you're on. Each left-hand page also includes a timeline, marked 'WHAT IN THE WORLD', which lists key dates and events in both science and world history between the page you're on and the one immediately before it. The few exceptions are where two consecutive subjects fall in the same year.

14 BILLION years ago
FORMATION OF THE UNIVERSE

IT is almost certain that the universe began with a 'Big Bang' just less than 14 billion years ago.

Before it, the universe was tiny, incredibly dense and unimaginably hot. All of space, time and energy were contained in an area almost infinitesimally small.

The universe suddenly expanded at an incredible rate, so that a tiny fraction of a second later it was a thousand billion billion kilometres across. The Big Bang was an explosion of space and time, not in space and time.

The universe continued to expand – though not quite so dramatically. As it did so, it cooled, and some of its energy 'condensed' into matter. After about 300,000 years, the universe had cooled enough for atoms of the element hydrogen to form, a thin veil of gas throughout space.

Gravity caused the hydrogen gas to clump together, forming galaxies filled with young stars. Those stars produce other elements while they are burning and yet more when they die, in spectacular explosions called supernovas.

Our own star – the sun – formed from the debris of a supernova about 4.5 billion years ago. Smaller clumps of gas and dust around the newborn sun became planets. One of those was rocky, and at just the right distance from the sun for life to develop. It is Earth. And now, one Earth species – our own – has enough intelligence to begin working out the whole incredible story.

In the 1920s, astronomers noticed that galaxies seem to be moving away from us in every direction. The further away they are, the faster they are moving. This can only be explained by the fact that the universe itself is expanding. The galaxies are being 'dragged apart' as space itself expands.

Fortunately, a theory already existed that could cope with the idea of an expanding universe. It is Einstein's General Theory of Relativity, published in 1915. During the 1920s, several scientists had used Einstein's theory to work out possible scenarios for the beginning of space and time. A Belgian monk and scientist, Georges Lemaître, first formed the idea of a Big Bang, or 'cosmic egg', as he called it.

During the 1950s, scientists realised that if the Big Bang really had happened, there would be a faint trace of microwave radiation left over from the immense heat of the early universe. It would have to be coming from all directions, filling every part of the universe. In 1964, American radio engineers Arno Penzias and Robert Wilson discovered that ancient echo of the Big Bang – the cosmic microwave background (CMB). It was exactly as predicted.

There are still problems with the Big Bang theory. One is that most of the matter in the universe seems to be 'dark matter', invisible to human science but known to exist because it exerts gravitational pull, just like visible matter. No one knows exactly what dark matter is, but it is vital to the understanding of the origin of our universe.

MIND BOGGLER
- If all the time since the Big Bang was condensed into one day, the dinosaurs would be wiped out at six minutes to midnight. Modern humans would appear just over a second before midnight.

Cosmic seeds Whole-sky temperature map of the cosmic background radiation, with data from NASA's WMAP project in 2003. It was in the cooler regions (blue) that matter clumped to form galaxies.

Tuning in Arno Penzias and Robert Wilson in front of the huge radio telescope antenna, with which they discovered the cosmic background radiation in 1964.

Supernova At the end of their lives, many stars heat up and explode, creating new elements and scattering them through space. New stars and planets are born from this debris.

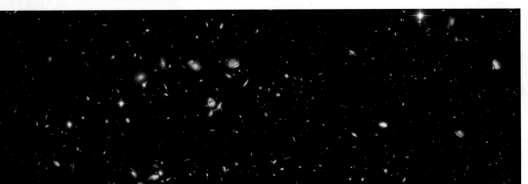

Deep sky This remarkable photograph was captured by the Hubble Space Telescope in 1994. Each of the interesting blobs in this picture is a galaxy. The light from the most distant travelled for more than 10,000 million years.

NOW JUMP TO... ➔ GALILEO page 28; ➔ EINSTEIN page 88; ➔ THE GALAXY page 92

THE Sun

Monday, November 23, 14591689406BC

BANG

FULL EXPLOSIVE STORY – PAGES 4-32

2.6m BC TOOLS: THE BIRTH OF TECHNOLOGY

STONE tools, first made about 2.6 million years ago, were the first ever invention – the birth of human technology.

The first people to make and use them were barely human at all – they were a human-like species called *Homo habilis* ('skilful person'). They lived a hard life hunting and gathering on the plains of Africa, so sharp-edged stone tools would have made a big difference to them as they killed and skinned animals.

About a million years later, a more developed species arose. It is called *Homo erectus*, because it stood more upright than its ancestors. *Homo erectus* was the first to use fire, and the first human-like species to migrate away from Africa. The first ever Britons were probably *Homo erectus* – populating the area around 500,000 years ago.

The species we most associate with being 'cave people' and using stone tools is *Homo neanderthalis*. The Neanderthals were widespread in Europe and lived during the very cold period from about 200,000 years ago until about 30,000 years ago. Only a few Neanderthals ever made it to Britain. It was only at the end of the last Ice Age, about 10,000 years ago, that modern humans – *Homo sapiens* – settled in any great number.

The period of human history in which people relied on stone tools is called the Stone Age. It is divided into the Palaeolithic era, or 'old stone age' and the Neolithic era or 'new stone

age'. Palaeolithic tools were basic, but they had a variety of uses: felling trees and woodworking, cutting and stripping animal hide, digging for roots – and later, killing animals and other Neanderthals. They were made by striking one piece of stone onto another, causing chips and flakes to fly off, leaving a sharp, serrated edge; often it was the flakes themselves that were used. Palaeolithic tools were made from many different types of rock, including quartz, flint and a volcanic rock called obsidian.

The Palaeolithic era ended with the birth of civilisation – the Neolithic era – which began at different times in different places between 8000 BC and 4500 BC. Tools became more sophisticated; they

were often smooth-edged, because most were ground down rather than 'flaked'. Neolithic people used stone tools to grind corn into flour; they also made fine stone drills and delicate jewellery. The Neolithic period ended when people began to make things from bronze instead of stone. This also happened at different times in different parts of the world, but generally around 3000 BC.

MIND BOGGLER

● Human DNA is more than 95 per cent identical to that of chimpanzees, our closest living relative. And chimps in a rain forest in Ivory Coast use stone tools to crack open nuts.

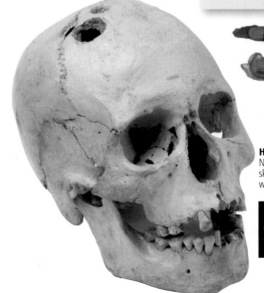

Caught knapping Artist's impression of *Homo habilis* striking two stones together to make a tool – a process known as knapping.

WHAT IN THE WORLD?

bya = billion years ago; **mya** = million years ago.

13.7 bya	Big Bang, the origin of the Universe.
4.5 bya	The Earth and other planets form, from the solar nebula, dust and gas around the new-born sun.
3 bya	The first primitive life on Earth.
600 mya	First worms and jellyfish.
390 mya	The first fish with backbones.
350 mya	The first insects and millipedes.
300 mya	The first amphibians.
260 mya	The first dinosaurs.
65 mya	Sudden extinction of all the dinosaurs.
7 mya	The human lineage breaks from other apes.
5 mya	The first hominids (human-like creatures) to walk on two legs.

Handy tool Palaeolithic hand tools, like this hand axe, were simple. They were produced by flaking pieces of rock to produce a sharp edge.

Smooth operator In the Neolithic period, stone tool making was more sophisticated. Tools like this axe head had smooth edges that were more accurately produced.

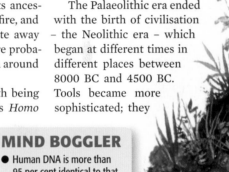

Hole in the head Replica flint-and-wood Neolithic drills, used make holes in living people's skulls. This technique is called trepanning, and was supposed to release evil spirits.

NOW JUMP TO...
● DARWIN page 64; ● SLICED BREAD page 98

...s ready .. hunter Ug

...ood of ...izmos ...o spare ...s hard ...rafting

HOMER BASE ...d BEE ANCUE

...new gadget will ...n the floodgates ...string of amaz- ...tools, it was pre- ...ed last night.

...me will simply ...nore efficient kill- ...machines.

...hers may be ...d to spruce up ...terrible drabness ...he average cave. ...nter Ug Grunter, ...said last night: ...rs Grunter's ...ays on at me to ...the place up.

Trendy

...But what with all ...deer I have to ...plus the lack of ...lements to work ..., when do I ever ...a chance?"

...g is a huge fan ...the flint tool ...ch makes it far ...ier to cut chunks ...meat from ani- ...s.

...also enables ...skins to be cut ...in seconds and ...le into warm, ...dy garments.

...g added: "Nor- ...ly this is so lab- ...intensive, one of ...big pains of the ...eolithic era. This ...er solves that."

CUTTING EDGE

Flint gadget 'will change our lives for ever'

SAY hello to the ultimate in new technology — a handy cutting device made from FLINT.

Astonishingly, anyone can make one.

But the labour-saving "tool", produced by hacking off a sliver using

By CHIP STONE

another rock, was last night tipped to change the course of history.

The secret lies in the gizmo's sharp edge. That gives it any number of uses including hunting, killing, skinning and more hunting and killing.

Whittle While You Work — Page 5

● 9

4500 BC THE WHEEL: GREATEST INVENTION IN HISTORY

THE WHEEL is often described as the most important invention of all time – it had a fundamental impact on transport and later on agriculture and industry.

The wheel-and-axle combination was invented around 4500 BC and was probably first used for a potter's wheel. The idea was quickly adapted for other uses – in particular on wagons and chariots.

For thousands of years, people used sledges to drag heavy loads. At some point, they realised that placing logs underneath the sledges enabled them to move along more easily. The wheel, fixed to the sledge, is an expansion of that idea.

On the earliest carts, the wheels were heavy, solid, and attached to the axle so the whole assembly turned together. Soon, it became common for the wheels to turn around a fixed axle. Wheels with spokes, first made around 2000 BC, were lighter, enabling vehicles to move faster.

Wheels were initially useful on carts and chariots pulled by oxen or horses. But humans discovered that a wheel powered by people, animals, wind or flowing water can be put to many other uses. Foot-powered spinning wheels appeared around 500 BC, water-wheels in the first century BC and windmills in the seventh century AD.

For centuries, waterwheels and windmills

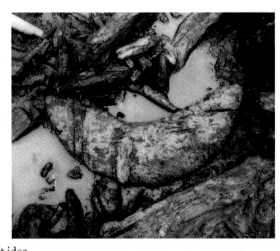

The turn of Britain The oldest known wheel in Britain, from between 1350 and 950 BC. It was discovered, preserved in a bog, at Flag Fen, near modern-day Peterborough – now a Bronze Age heritage site.

helped irrigate fields or remove water from flooded areas; they drove grinding machines to produce flour; they powered bellows and hammers in metal workshops. During the 17th and 18th centuries, water-wheels powered huge machines in cotton mills. Eventually, the steam engine became the preferred source of power to turn the wheels of industry.

There are many candidates for the most important invention of all time. Many of them – including the wheel – were developed in early civilisations.

Towards the end of the Stone Age people had begun to settle in small communities in many parts of the world. Instead of hunting and gathering, they farmed the land and kept animals. As settlements grew, people had more time to wonder about how the world works and to develop new technologies and techniques such as metalworking. Stone gave way to bronze – a hard mixture of copper and tin – and the Stone Age became the Bronze Age.

Several of the most important early civilisations were in Mesopotamia, a large area between the Tigris and Euphrates rivers covering much of what is now Iraq. Historians often call Mesopotamia the 'cradle of civilisation'. The city-states of this region had governments and laws, they had mathematicians and

WHAT IN THE WORLD?

1 million BC	*Homo erectus* learns to control fire.
250,000 BC	Our species, *Homo sapiens*, is born in Africa.
70,000 BC	Primitive oil lamps are used.
60,000 BC	Humans migrate to Europe and Asia.
40,000 BC	Humans migrate to Australia and New Zealand.
35,000 BC	The first cave paintings.
20,000 BC	Sewing needles are first used, in France.
20,000 BC	Humans migrate from Siberia to the Americas, probably across the Bering Strait.
10,000 BC	The end of the last Ice Age.
9000 BC	The first farmers, in what is now the Middle East; domestication of dogs, goats and sheep.
8000 BC	The first mud-brick buildings, in Mesopotamia.
7000 BC	The first clay pots.
6000 BC	The first towns and cities.

Sharpest tool Metals can be beaten to form a sharp edge, and can be cast into intricate shapes. This ancient bronze chisel head was found in Norfolk.

astronomers, and their inhabitants developed calendars, writing and systems of measurement. The wheel was invented in Mesopotamia, and bronze was first used there.

Other early civilisations also grew up around big rivers. In Ancient Egypt it was the Nile; in Ancient India, the Indus; in China, the Huang He (Yellow River). All of them flood every year, making low-lying areas dependably fertile.

Major technologies that developed in all these early civilisations include primitive timekeeping (water clocks and sundials), metalworking and glassmaking.

In Bronze Age Britain, people settled in small tribes, not a widespread, organised civilisation. Travellers from civilisations abroad introduced new technologies, including the wheel.

MIND BOGGLER
● At 100 kilometres per hour (60mph), a wheel on a typical family car turns about 13 times a second.

Reinventing the wheel Spoke-wheeled chariots, used in warfare, could travel at speeds of up to 65 kilometres per hour (40 mph).

What a drag Neolithic people made sledges, dugout canoes and bows-and-arrows using their stone tools. Later sledges had runners to reduce friction between the sledge and the ground.

NOW JUMP TO... ● STEPHENSON'S ROCKET page 56; ● THE MOTOR CAR page 74

THE Sun

turday, August 11, 4502BC

THE NEW 'ROLLER'

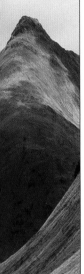

er threat . . . a hill

llages n hills rotest: is is a saster

LEN DROVER

OP villages were
us last night,
ing the "roller"
be the death of
communities.

y say they will
be able to com-
with settlements
e plain once the
transport system
and running.

e village elder
"Of course, a
g sledge will
marvellous when
e at the top and
to get down fast.
t try dragging it
up again at the
f the day.

e've always loved
uphill — you
see the enemy
g a mile off.

t no one's going
ant to stay up
when they can
around so easily
there."

inventors of the
r" threw hillfolk
line last night.

y said it might
ssible to coax an
al into pulling a
g sledge uphill.

Spinning circles may be answer to world's transport nightmare

THIS is the first picture of the new device hailed as the answer to the world's transport problems.

The round wooden objects can be placed at either end of a pole and allowed to spin.

When fixed to the bottom of — for example — a sledge, they allow the entire contraption to "roll" along at considerable speed. In fact it can

By AUSTIN ALLEGRO, Transport Editor

cover 100 yards in a fraction of the time an ox takes to drag a sledge the same distance.

Using the devices — being dubbed "rollers" — people can travel much further than before, taking as little as a **DAY** to reach the next settlement. But one safety campaigner said: "How do they stop? This hasn't been fully thought through."

It'll Never Catch On — Clarkson, Page 21

1800 BC EXTRACTION OF IRON A TOUGH NEW METAL

IRON is the most abundant metal on Earth and by far the one most used by man. It is cheap, strong and extremely versatile – but humans were only able to refine it 5,000 years ago, long after they were using lead and copper.

Metals are usually contained in compounds called ores, found in rocks, and were highly prized in early civilisations. Early humans occasionally came across pieces of gold, silver and copper which, unlike almost all other metals, occur in their pure state as well as in ores.

A process known as smelting is used to extract metals from their ores. People first smelted iron ore more than 5,000 years ago. In the second millenium BC, iron began to replace bronze and copper for making weapons and tools.

In an ore, metal atoms are bound to those of other elements such as oxygen. Smelting involves heating an ore with carbon – early smelters used charcoal, which is nearly pure carbon. The carbon combines with the oxygen, producing carbon dioxide and carbon monoxide gases, and leaving molten metal behind.

Lead was smelted in Anatolia (now Turkey) around 6500 BC, and copper in about 3600 BC in Mesopotamia. No one knows where or when iron was first smelted, but it may have been as early as 3000 BC, in the Hittite Empire, again in part of what is now Turkey.

Evidence of early iron smelting has also been found in Egypt, in Mesopotamia and, a few hundred years later, West Africa. In each location it caught on quickly, being so much more

> ### MIND BOGGLER
> ● The first iron ever used came from outer space – extracted from meteorites that landed on Earth.

versatile than bronze. Iron is rarely produced pure: it is usually converted into steel – an alloy of iron and carbon. Steel can be made much stronger than iron or bronze.

Smelting iron needs higher temperatures than copper. Initially, bellows were used to make furnaces hotter. In about 100 BC, Chinese inventors found a way to blast air from below, making the ores smelt more efficiently. Blast furnaces are still an important part of iron and steel making today.

Iron and steel quickly became indispensable across the world, as techniques improved and spread. Steel

Steel will The Bessemer converter, a huge vessel for converting low-grade steel into high-grade steel, was invented by Henry Bessemer in 1855.

was to play a vital role in the industrialisation of Britain. In 1709, shortly before the start of the Industrial Revolution, English entrepreneur Abraham Darby (1678–1717) began using coke, made from coal, rather than charcoal, made from wood. Around 1750, his son, also Abraham (1711–1763), began to produce good quality steel in large quantities.

In 1783 another Englishman, Henry Cort (1740–1800), invented a process called puddling, which produces 'wrought iron', less brittle than the 'pig iron' used previously. The steel making process was further improved and industrialised in 1855 when English engineer Henry Bessemer (1813–1898) found a way to burn off excess carbon, converting low grade steel into just the right mixture in huge quantities.

The 18th and 19th centuries were filled with discoveries of many more metals. Aluminium, now cheap and plentiful, was unknown before 1808. It was produced in the 1820s, but only in small quantities. Weight-for-weight, it was more expensive than gold. Today, aluminium is extracted from its ore using powerful electric currents – a process developed in 1886 and which led to its large-scale commercialisation.

But despite the discovery of metals such as aluminium, iron still accounts for more than 90 per cent of all metals produced.

Light metal Once more valuable than gold, aluminium is now so cheap that it can be cast into large items like engine blocks.

Hot air During the Middle Ages, iron was produced in small blast furnaces like the one in this picture taken from an influential German book on metallurgy, published in 1555.

Fire in the hills This oil painting, *Coalbrookdale by Night*, shows Abraham Darby's steelworks, in Shropshire. Darby's coke smelting process revolutionised steel production.

WHAT IN THE WORLD?

3500 BC	Metal mirrors are used in Egypt.
3500 BC	The Egyptians first use papyrus.
3000 BC	Cotton is grown and harvested in Mexico.
2900 BC	Cotton cultivation in India; the first tooth fillings in Mesopotamia.
2850 BC	The Great Pyramid is built, at Giza, Egypt.
2800 BC	First version of Stonehenge is completed.
2700 BC	Primitive stone arches are built in Mesopotamia.
2600 BC	Primitive sundial clocks, in Egypt.
2450 BC	Agreed weights and measures in Mesopotamia.
2000 BC	First wheels with spokes.
1900 BC	Mesopotamian mathematicians discover what is now known as Pythagoras' Theorem.
1450 BC	The Egyptians build water clocks.

NOW JUMP TO... ➲ PLASTICS page 108; ➲ INDUSTRIAL REVOLUTION page 56

THE Sun

Wednesday, April 17, 1823BC

b'Zarre METAL & ROCK SPECIAL PAGES 16&17

ORESOME

Now we can make iron...out of ROCK

By BERNIE HANDS, Assistant Editor (Smelting)

IRON can be made from ROCK, it was sensationally announced last night.

The supertough metal is extracted from iron ore by "smelting" – subjecting it to immense heat.

It is likely to mean a revolution in weapons and tools, made up to now with softer metals like copper and bronze. One expert said: "I can see this launching a new age in mankind's history. But we'll have to watch it doesn't lead to a huge increase in terrifying new weapons."

Ore: What Is It Good For? The Big Debate, See Page 2

420 BC DEMOCRITUS AND THE CONCEPT OF THE ATOM

THE GREEK philosopher Democritus was not the first person to suggest matter is made of tiny particles: Indian philosophers had suggested it two centuries earlier, and Democritus borrowed his theory from his teacher. But it was Democritus who was influential when scientists finally accepted the idea – 2,000 years after his death.

Democritus (c. 450–370 BC)

Democritus (c. 450–370 BC) suggested that particles move about, group and regroup, but never change. He described them with the Greek word atomos, meaning 'indivisible': you can't cut them, and you can't destroy them. To Democritus, a chemical reaction or a physical change such as melting is just a rearrangement of particles. The space between the particles is completely empty: what the philosophers called 'the void'.

About 50 years later another philosopher, Aristotle (384–322 BC), came up with a different theory about matter. He suggested that substances do change in chemical reactions, and although he admitted that there might be a 'smallest amount' of substance, he believed that matter is continuous – not made of tiny separate pieces. Aristotle also objected to the idea of the void. In the Middle Ages, universities taught Aristotle's views about the world as fact.

During the 16th and 17th centuries, people began to question the teachings of Aristotle. In 1649, French priest Pierre Gassendi (1592–1695) translated an Ancient Greek book into Latin, the language used by most scientists at the time. The book included an explanation of Democritus' idea, and Gassendi was impressed. He spread the word, and largely thanks to him, the particle view of matter became popular.

The 17th century also saw the rise of experimental science. In 1643, Italian physicist Evangalista Torricelli (1608–1647) invented the mercury barometer – a closed tube filled with mercury sitting in a dish of mercury. At the top of the tube was a space that was apparently empty – the void, whose existence Aristotle denied. Actually, that space is filled with rarefied mercury vapour, but scientists didn't know that at the time, and it helped to give weight to the particle view.

In 1662, Anglo-Irish physicist Robert Boyle (1626–1691) discovered that if you double the pressure on a gas, you squash it to half its volume – a relationship known as Boyle's Law. That is exactly how a gas would behave if it were made of particles moving freely in all directions.

English meteorologist and chemist John Dalton (1766–1844) devised the first modern atomic theory. He said there was only one type of atom for each chemical element, they are different from those of other elements, they are indestructible and can combine with other types of atom to form compounds. He even managed to estimate the relative weights of the different atoms.

By the middle of the 18th century, most scientists had accepted what Democritus had suggested two millennia earlier – that matter is made of tiny, indivisible particles in constant motion. This is a very good starting point in understanding matter. But we now know that things are a lot more complicated.

WHAT IN THE WORLD?

776 BC The first Olympic Games are held, in Greece.
650 BC The first coins are made, in Asia and in Greece.
600 BC The first sundials are used, in China.
580 BC Thales of Miletus (c. 624–548 BC) suggests that water is the basis of all matter.
530 BC Anaximenes of Miletus (c. 570–510 BC) suggests that air is the basis of all matter.
480 BC Heraclitus of Ephesus (c. 540–475 BC) suggests that fire is the basis of all matter.
509 BC The founding of the Roman Republic, which later becomes the Roman Empire.
438 BC The Parthenon, in Athens, is completed.

MIND BOGGLER

● Ten million atoms side by side would span one millimetre. No one saw one until 1981 when Gerd Binnig and Heinrich Rohrer did using a 'scanning tunnelling microscope'.

Elementary idea Dalton's list of elements, 1803. Several of the substances Dalton listed as elements are actually compounds.

ELEMENTS

⊙ Hydrogen	7		Strontian	
Azote	5		Barytes	
● Carbon	54	Ⓘ Iron		
○ Oxygen	7	Ⓩ Zinc		
Phosphorus	9	Ⓒ Copper		
⊕ Sulphur	13	Ⓛ Lead		
Magnesia	20	Ⓢ Silver		
⊖ Lime	24	Gold		
◑ Soda	28	Ⓟ Platina		
◐ Potash	42	Mercury		

Reading matter In 1661, Robert Boyle argued strongly in favour of the idea that matter is made of particles, in his popular book *The Sceptical Chymist*.

THE
SCEPTICAL CHYMIST:
OR
CHYMICO-PHYSICAL
Doubts & Paradoxes,
Touching the
SPAGYRIST'S PRINCIPLES
Commonly call'd
HYPOSTATICAL;
As they are wont to be Propos'd and
Defended by the Generality of
ALCHYMISTS.
Whereunto is præmis'd Part of another Discourse
relating to the same Subject.
BY
The Honourable ROBERT BOYLE, Esq.

LONDON,
Printed by J. Cadwell for J. Crooke, and are to be
Sold at the Ship in St. Paul's Church-Yard.
MDCLXI.

Nothing to discuss Torricelli's barometer. Atmospheric pressure supports the column of mercury inside the glass tube – but only up to about 76 cm. Above that, there appears to be nothing at all.

The Earth is round

People in early civilisations believed Earth was flat. But several Ancient Greek philosophers reasoned that a round, or spherical, Earth made more sense. Around 390 BC, Plato (c. 427–347 BC) went as far as to suggest that there are other lands on the opposite side of the Earth, which he called 'Antipodes'. Later, Aristotle made several observations that settled the question. For example, he noticed that ships disappear over the horizon, hull first – if the Earth were flat, they would simply get smaller and smaller.

We now know Earth is a slightly flattened sphere – an 'oblate spheroid'. The diameter from pole-to-pole (12,712 kilometres) is 44 kilometres less than the diameter at the equator.

NOW JUMP TO... ➲ ALCHEMY & CHEMISTRY page 18; ➲ ATOMIC THEORY page 96

THE Sun

One coin

Monday, November 5, 420BC

EARTH 'ROUND' SHOCK

EARTH is round, Greek philosophers claim. They say it cannot be flat (left) because:

● Ships disappear over a horizon instead of getting smaller and vanishing as they would if the sea was flat.

● Earth's shadow on the moon is curved from any angle, only possible with a sphere.

Edge Trimmers — Page 2

WOULD YOU ATOM AND EVE IT!

Greek: We're made of tiny bits

Giggler . . . Democritus

EVERYTHING on Earth is made up of tiny bits called "atoms", it was claimed last night.

Respected Greek philosopher Democritus says they are invisible — and the smallest thing that exists anywhere.

They buzz around in space, which he calls "the void", until they combine with other atoms to form objects or beings. Democritus, dubbed

EXCLUSIVE by MOLLY CULE

the Laughing Philosopher because of his constant cheer, is about 30. His theories carry a lot of weight because he is so well-educated and widely travelled.

He believes cheerfulness is life's ultimate goal, calling it "a state in which the soul lives peacefully and tranquilly, undisturbed by fear, superstition or other feeling."

*He's Having A Laugh
— The Sun Says, Page 8*

Join the dots . . . our painting shows how bloke would look if you could see his atoms

● 15

240 BC THE GREAT MINDS OF ANCIENT GREECE

ANCIENT Greece was an immensely fertile producer of philosophers who pondered such fundamental questions as the meaning and origins of life. Some of their theories were way ahead of their time, but Archimedes and Eratosthenes were among very few to back them up with experimental evidence.

Ancient Greece, as it is now known, thrived from around 900BC to 30BC and extended far beyond Greece itself. Many of its important figures lived on far-flung lands around the eastern Mediterranean. It was not quite an empire – though its influence was often spread by conquering neighbouring states. Ancient Greece was a culture, a way of life.

One of its main intellectual centres was Alexandria, on the northern coast of Egypt. It boasted a huge library containing hundreds of thousands of scrolls – the ideas and observations of Ancient Greece's greatest thinkers.

Eratosthenes (c. 276 BC–194 BC) was head librarian, but he was also an accomplished mathematician, astronomer and geographer. Modern academics disagree on the accuracy of his calculation of the Earth's circumference because they are not sure about the value of 'stadia', the units he used. But one 'stadion' was normally about 185 metres – and with that value Eratosthenes' result was very close to the actual figure.

Influential thinking Aristotle formulated theories about everything from the weather to the origin of life – but, like so many of his fellow natural philosophers, he never tested them.

MIND BOGGLER

● Archimedes is said by legend to have used mirrors to torch a Roman fleet besieging Syracuse – deflecting the sun's rays on to the highly-flammable tar which waterproofed the hulls.

Archimedes (c. 287 BC–212 BC) was a friend of Eratosthenes. The two men met at Alexandria, though Archimedes spent most of his life in his birthplace – a Greek port in Sicily called Syracuse. He was well known in his day, mainly for designing huge machines to defend Syracuse against invading Roman warships.

As a physicist, Archimedes discovered the concept of the centre of gravity, and analysed how levers and pulleys work. But his greatest contributions were in mathematics – he was centuries ahead of his time – and in applying mathematics to the real world.

The incident involving his bath is famous, but probably only a legend. It relates to his discovery of what is now known as Archimedes' Principle, which states that a submerged object is pushed upwards by a force equal to the weight of the fluid it displaces.

Previous civilisations created myths to explain how the world works, and Ancient Greek 'scientists' were keen to replace them with more rational explanations. They were not true scientists: most refused to test their theories on the grounds that experiments are artificial situations removed from the real world. Today, rigorous testing of new theories with meticulous experiments is central to modern science. Any new research must also

Circles in the sky Eratosthenes invented the armillary sphere, a model of the Universe with the Earth at the centre. This one was made nearly 1700 years after his death.

be checked by other scientists before it can be published – a process called 'peer review'.

Perhaps the most famous Greek philosopher was Aristotle (384–322 BC). He devised hundreds of explanations about the natural world, space, the nature of matter, and forces and motion. Unfortunately, many of his ideas were wrong but were taught to students of 'natural philosophy' for hundreds of years, and challenged only during the Renaissance period in 16th and 17th century Europe.

Ancient Greek culture had a strong influence on the emerging Roman Empire. But as the Western half of the Roman Empire fell in the 5th century AD, most of the accumulated Greek and Roman knowledge was lost. The library at Alexandria had been destroyed, and the Western world hurtled into a period of disorganisation and conflict often called 'the Dark Ages'.

Good doctor Bust of Hippocrates (c. 460 BC – 377 BC), another revolutionary thinker in Ancient Greece, who rejected superstitious ideas about disease, and put medicine on a scientific footing.

WHAT IN THE WORLD?

395 BC Greek philosopher Plato (c. 427–347 BC) invents a water clock with an alarm.

340 BC Aristotle writes that space is never empty – 'nature abhors a vacuum'.

332 BC Macedonian emperor Alexander the Great (356–323 BC) founds Alexandria, in Egypt.

312 BC Roman engineers build the first ever aqueduct (artificial water supply channel), to serve the city of Rome.

300 BC Greek mathematician Euclid (c. 325–265 BC) publishes *Elements*, which becomes the standard geometry textbook for the next 2,000 years.

295 BC Greek physicians Herophilus (335-280 BC) and Erasistratus (c. 330–250 BC) perform public dissections of human bodies.

290 BC The first convex lenses are made, in Carthage (modern day Tunisia).

270 BC Chinese engineers invent bellows that can produce a continuous stream of air.

260 BC Mayan mathematicians in South America are the first to use 'zero' and a place value number system like our own.

255 BC Construction of the Great Wall of China begins.

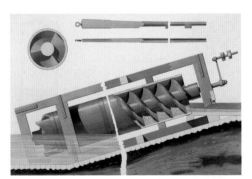

Clever machine Archimedes' screw, his most famous invention, lifts water when it turns. This device was used in irrigation and pumping out floodwater.

NOW JUMP TO... ❯ GALILEO page 24; ❯ ANATOMY page 30

THE Sun

Thursday, July 7, 240BC   One coin

YOU STREAKER

Outrage at Archimedes' naked dash

MATHS genius Archimedes caused outrage yesterday by dashing naked through the streets shouting at the top of his voice.

The 47-year-old eccentric shocked neighbours in Syracuse, Sicily, by yelling "Eureka", meaning: "I've found it."

Archimedes, famous for his "screw" device which raises water from a low to a high level, had been in his tub moments earlier. Last night he apologised for the incident. But he absurdly claimed that he

EXCLUSIVE by KIT ORFF

could not contain himself once he realised the amount of water he displaced in his bath was equal to the volume of that part of his body which was submerged.

One angry neighbour said: "That won't wash. I don't care how clever he is or how excited he got in his bath. Grown men do not run down the street naked."

Load of Flannel — Page Nine

I've got big nudes... Archimedes springing from his bath yesterday

---

Greek uses Sun to figure out distance round Earth

PLANET GIRTH

By TERRY FIRMA

A TOP astronomer has worked out Earth's circumference with incredible accuracy, it was revealed last night.

The measurement is 252,000 stadia.

The Greek maths genius, known only as Eratosthenes, calculated the figure using the Sun!

Eratosthenes, 36, knew that the celestial ball of flame is directly over Syene, Egypt, at noon on the summer solstice.

But at his home town of Alexandria it is seven degrees south at the same time.

Knowing Alexandria is due north of Syene — and that a full circle is 360°, he says the distance between them must be 7/360 of the Earth's circumference.

And since he knows it is 5,000 stadia between the two cities, he can work out how far it is round the planet.

Eratosthenes has so far only been known as a poet and head of the Alexandria library.

One geographer said last night: "Obviously it's hard to test his calculation at this point. But we think it will stand the test of time."

Ruler of the Earth — Page 11

ARAB ALCHEMY AND EARLY CHEMISTRY

ARAB scholar Jabir ibn Hayyan is famous for his 'invention' of the Philosophers' Stone – purportedly a substance which could turn ordinary metals into gold. He never found such a substance – but he did develop important laboratory techniques still used today.

Although no one doubts the existence of Jabir ibn Hayyan (c. 721–c. 815), some of his work may have been carried out by others writing under his name. Even if some of his story is legend rather than fact, it illustrates the contribution Arab scholars made to chemistry, mathematics and astronomy.

Among Hayyan's inventions are a safe method of distillation and a way to make crystals; he also discovered several important chemicals – including hydrochloric and nitric acids. Perhaps most importantly, his writing encouraged others to experiment methodically with chemicals with the same care and enthusiasm as he did.

Hayyan was an accomplished physicist and astronomer, but best known as an alchemist. Alchemy was the quest to control the transformation of matter – in particular, to make ordinary metals into precious ones. Alchemists used the techniques and materials of metallurgists (metal workers), but the ideas of philosophers; Hayyan's alchemical principles can be traced directly to the Greek philosopher Aristotle (384–322 BC).

Like many other early philosophers, Aristotle believed all matter was composed of just four elements: water, air, earth and fire. Each could transform into the others – so by making chemicals react in just the right way you should be able to effect any transformation, even making lead into gold. We now know each metal is a different element, and elements do not change during chemical reactions.

Hayyan lived in the flourishing Islamic Empire. The rise of Islam in the 7th century had united the mainly Arabic-speaking peoples of North Africa, Persia and Syria into a formidable civilisation. The Arabs traded with China and India and learned about those cultures' science and technology. They also moved into several places once part of Ancient Greece, which is how they came across Aristotle's work. But Arab mathematicians, astronomers, doctors and alchemists were not content simply to inherit other civilisations' ideas: they made significant contributions of their own.

In the 12th century, Arabs in Spain and Southern Italy translated the knowledge they had gathered into Latin, the language of the Roman Catholic Church across Europe. Aristotle's teaching, which had survived unchanged, was taught without question in the European universities of the Middle Ages for about 500 years.

In the 17th century scientists began to challenge Aristotle's ideas about matter. English clergyman Joseph Priestley (1733–1804) discovered a total of eight different gases, proving that air is a mixture of substances and not an element.

In 1766 another English chemist, Henry Cavendish (1731–1810), discovered that when hydrogen burns in oxygen it makes water, another of Aristotle's 'elements'. In the 1780s, pioneering French chemist Antoine Lavoisier (1743–1794) made sense of elements, compounds and chemical reactions, and founded modern chemistry.

During the 19th century, scientists began to work out what makes atoms of one element

Chemical separation One of the oldest surviving examples of an alembic (from the 10th century) – an apparatus for distillation, which was invented by Jabir ibn Hayyan.

different from atoms of others. Russian chemist Dmitri Mendeleev (1834–1907) took the first step in 1869, when he grouped the elements according to their chemical properties, making the first periodic table.

Chemical pioneer French chemist Antoine Lavoisier, who defined the modern concepts of element and compound.

> **MIND BOGGLER**
> ● *Harry Potter and the Philosopher's Stone* launched JK Rowling's series of books which have current worldwide sales of 300 million. In the book, boy wizard Harry foils an attempt to steal the stone, which can bestow eternal life.

WHAT IN THE WORLD?

190 BC Concrete is first used, by the Romans in Italy.
170 BC In Rome, the first paved roads appear.
100 BC The Silk Route – a trading passage from China to the West – is established.
90 BC Chinese mathematicians are the first to use negative numbers; Great Wall of China finished.
c. 3 BC Birth of Jesus Christ.
43 The Romans invade Britain.
79 Eruption of Mount Vesuvius destroys Pompeii and Herculanium.
122 Hadrian's Wall is built by Roman soldiers to defend Roman Britain from northern tribes.
140 Astronomer Ptomlemy (Claudius Ptolemaeus) writes astronomy textbook commonly known as *Almagest*, the standard astronomy text for the next 1,400 years.
132 Chinese inventor Zhang Heng makes the world's first earthquake detector.
c. 350 A primitive magnetic compass is used in China.
c. 500 The Early Middle Ages begin in Europe after the downfall of the Roman Empire there in 476.
c. 600 Whole-page printing, with wood blocks, is introduced in China.
632 The death of the Prophet Muhammad.
c. 650 The first windmills, in Persia.

Elementary work Russian chemist Dmitri Mendeleev, the first person to organise the chemical elements into a periodic table.

NOW JUMP TO... ➔ **THE CONCEPT OF THE ATOM page 14;** ➔ **NUCLEAR FISSION page 102**

ETERNAL LIFE 'MELTDOWN' FOR PENSIONS

By DES PERATION, Pensions Editor

ETERNAL life would be a DISASTER for old folk — because no one could ever save enough cash to retire on. A pensions expert said: "It's bad enough now, and life expectancy's only 45."

Coping With Poverty and Squalor — See Sun Money

Fed-up . . . a wrinkly

rew's a clever boy . . . alchemist Jabir holds aloft a flask of mysterious chemicals as devoted followers watch in awe last night   Picture: WALTER CULLA

Arab swotter and the Philosophers' Stone

EXCLUSIVE by FINN STOREY

A MYSTERY substance has the power to create eternal life and turn any metal into gold, a top chemist claimed last night.

Arab Jabir ibn Hayyan says the magical powder is made from something called the "Philoso-

'MY POWDER MAKES GOLD'

phers' Stone". A liquid called an "elixir", made from the same substance, is thought to be able to stave off death. But Jabir, 55, has not produced the stone — or even hinted where it is. However, he is highly educated and has many followers who hang on his every word.

Jabir Writes For The Sun — Page 8

1267 GUNPOWDER AND THE HISTORY OF GUNS

GUNPOWDER was the first explosive – and ushered in a new era of weaponry. The English friar and philosopher Roger Bacon was the first in Europe to describe its formula – and within decades the first gun was invented.

Bacon (c. 1214–1294), nicknamed Doctor Mirabilis ('Wonderful Teacher' in Latin), was a Franciscan friar who championed experimental science.

He followed the teachings of the Western Catholic Church but had an extensive knowledge of other cultures – in particular Islamic physicists, mathematicians and alchemists.

Bacon learned about gunpowder, thought to have been invented by the Chinese some time before the 9th century, from its description in books by Arab scholars. He detailed how to make it in his 1242 book *On the Marvelous Power of Art and Nature*.

It is likely the Chinese produced gunpowder by accident. In their search for 'elixirs' to give eternal life or transform ordinary metals into gold, they must have combined its three ingredients, carbon, sulphur and nitrate – also known as saltpetre

The main feature of explosives is that they burn rapidly, producing copious amounts of waste gases. These expand quickly and can propel objects at high speed or break apart rocks.

Chinese soldiers used gunpowder as early as the 10th century in 'fire arrows' similar to today's firework rockets. By the 13th century,

Flintlock pistols, 19th century The most successful way to ignite the gunpowder in muskets and pistols before the 1840s was with sparks produced when flint hit a steel plate.

they were using it in bronze cannons. When European military leaders saw cannons in the 14th century, they quickly began using them too. They also developed battle rockets carrying an explosive over distances of two or three kilometres – though not with great accuracy.

In the 15th century, European soldiers began using muskets – firearms loaded from the open end of the barrel. They remained the weapon of choice until the invention of the cartridge in the 19th century. A cartridge consists of the bullet, the gunpowder and a primer charge that ignites when struck, causing the gunpowder to explode. Cartridges made it possible to use firearms in all weathers and to load them from the other end of the barrel.

Rifles took over from muskets in the 19th century – they have spiral grooves in the barrel to make the bullet spin, giving better stability.

MIND BOGGLER
- Until the 19th century, human waste was a valuable product because its high nitrogen content made it a source of saltpetre.

WHAT IN THE WORLD?

825 Arab mathematician Al-Khowarizmi writes his book about equations *Al-Jabr wa'l muqabalah*, known in the West as *Algebra*.

1015 Arab physicist Abu 'Ali Al-Hasan ibn Al-Haytham (Alhazen) correctly explains how lenses and curved mirrors work.

1066 King Harold is killed at Battle of Hastings; the victor, William the Conqueror, becomes king.

1086 King William orders a comprehensive survey of England, the Domesday Book.

1096 The beginning of the First Crusade, in which the Christian Church was to take control of Jerusalem from its Muslim rulers.

Black powder Traditional gunpowder has been replaced by smokeless explosives in weaponry, but is still used in many types of firework.

NOW JUMP TO... ➲ **ALFRED NOBEL page 78;** ➲ **ROCKETRY page 82**

Visionary friar

Like almost every other learned person at the time, Roger Bacon followed the teachings of the Western Catholic Church. But he also had extensive knowledge of other cultures besides the one dominated by his Church. In particular, his extensive knowledge of Islamic physicists, mathematicians and alchemists made him appreciate the importance of experimentation in science.

Stick with it Nitroglycerin can explode with sudden movements. But when absorbed into clay or paper, to make dynamite, it is safe to handle. Dynamite was invented by Alfred Nobel in 1867.

Two powerful new explosives were invented in the 19th century: nitrocellulose and nitroglycerin. Both produce much less smoke than gunpowder – they are the main constituents of 'smokeless powder' still used in cartridges today.

In the 1860s, Swedish chemist Alfred Nobel (1833–1896) combined liquid nitroglycerin with clay to form dynamite.

Today, there is a wide range of explosives, with firearms still their main area of application. But explosives have a peaceful use, too, in quarrying and the building of canals, tunnels and railway cuttings.

Automatic idea Hiram Maxim (1840–1916; bearded) who invented the machine gun in 1883. He sold his invention to every major military power, just in time for World War I.

LENSES 'FIX SIGHT'

PEOPLE with dodgy sight could soon see perfectly with this bizarre contraption which the Chinese are said to be wearing over their eyes. The device uses glass lenses, which Roger Bacon is also known to be working on.

Full Story — Page 5

FRIAR BACON UNVEILS 'GUN' POWDER

SIZZLE SIZZLE BOOM

By CATHERINE WHEEL, Defence Editor

A NEW explosive black powder could be used to make bombs to throw at our enemies, it was revealed last night.

Friar Roger Bacon *(below)* — one of Britain's cleverest men — describes the amazing substance in a new book, and says the crafty Chinese already use it.

The 53-year-old West Country holy man, based at a French monastery, even details how to make the stuff.

Bang Goes Peace — Centre Pages

---

utrage safety xperts ver DIY uide to ombs

MMY AUTOMATIC

TY campaigners furious yesterday Bacon publishing s on how to the explosive.

said: "This is a nt instruction al for any lunatic wants to make a . Who knows it could lead? s only two years we set up our Parliament. What ne nut decides to it up?"

re are already ing reports that hinese are devel- a "gun" — a -held weapon uses the pow- o shoot a projec- om a metal tube ge speed.

Wittering

one standing in way would be ed or even killed. campaigner ed: "I have no le with Friar n wittering on lenses, maths he stars.

don't have any em if he wants to his days dream- f so-called micro- es, telescopes flying machines steam ships.

t this powder is ad business. It s no purpose than to blow up. one is going to rt."

ACON: S HE A AD EGG?

EE PAGE 8

●21

1455 MASSIVE INFLUENCE OF THE PRINTING PRESS

THE PRINTING press was one of the most important and influential inventions of all time. It spread knowledge and ideas to more people, more cheaply and more quickly than ever before. It fuelled the Renaissance, during which scientists, inventors, philosophers and artists changed the world.

Before Johannes Gutenberg perfected his printing press in the 1440s, all books in Europe were produced by hand – every word had to be written out, mostly by monks or other scribes in monasteries. Books were extremely expensive, took a long time to make, and production was completely controlled by the Church.

WHAT IN THE WORLD?

1288 The first known gun is made, in China.

1297 William 'Braveheart' Wallace and his men rout the English army at the Battle of Stirling Bridge.

1305 The Taxis family begins the first private postal service, in Europe.

1310 The first mechanical clocks appear in Europe – nearly 600 years after the first mechanical clocks in China.

1314 Football is banned in England, because it is too violent; Battle of Bannockburn assures the independence of Scotland from England.

1340 The first blast furnace is built, in Belgium.

1340s The Black Death kills around 30 million people in Europe.

1386 Geoffrey Chaucer begins writing his *Canterbury Tales*.

1397 Richard 'Dick' Whittington is elected Mayor of London.

1408 Windmills are used for the first time to drain water from low-lying areas, in Holland.

1415 Henry V is victorious in the Battle of Agincourt, part of the Hundred Years' War.

1434 River Thames freezes over in London.

Typecast inventor Johannes Gutenberg was born in Mainz, Germany, about 1398, and died there around 1468.

A single copy of the Bible – the most commonly produced book at the time – normally took three years to make. Gutenberg's press could print hundreds in the same time.

It had a large wooden handle attached to a screw thread. When the handle was pulled, the letters to be printed – the type – pressed against a sheet of paper lying underneath. The letters were raised, like on a rubber stamp, and were coated with ink before each impression. This kind of printing is called 'letterpress'.

The most important aspect of Gutenberg's invention was 'moveable type': each letter, number or punctuation mark was made of a small, individual metal block. These were arranged into words and set into a larger block for printing over and over again.

Like most inventions, Gutenberg's press was not entirely new. Printing originated in China some time in the 6th or 7th century. Early Chinese printing used carved wooden blocks. Even moveable type had been thought up before – in China and Korea – in the 12th and 13th centuries. But Gutenberg combined several ideas, threw in some of his own and changed the world.

Hot metal Ladle (above), used to pour molten alloy into moulds to form letters, numbers and punctuation marks (right) for letterpress printing.

His timing was perfect. In the 15th century Europe was on the brink of a revolution in thinking: the Renaissance. Within decades of Gutenberg's first successful prints, presses were running in many cities across Europe. Books became much cheaper and more available; scientists published their ideas; philosophers inspired people with new ways of looking at things. New ideas spread like wildfire and more and more people learned to read.

Gutenberg's letterpress printing is cumbersome compared with modern printing technologies, and hardly used. Most books, newspapers and magazines are now printed by huge machines with sheets of paper moving continuously at high speed. These machines can print in full colour using 'offset lithography'. This uses flat, not raised, plates. The ink is transferred in two stages: from the flat plate to a rubber blanket, then from the blanket to the paper. Both plate and blanket are wrapped around rollers, which are in contact with other inked rollers.

For making just a few books or magazines, digital printing is increasingly popular. Digital printers are controlled directly from computers, and normally use static electric charge to attract the ink to the right parts of the paper.

MIND BOGGLER

● In a 1631 printing of the Bible the word 'not' was left out of the seventh commandment, making it read: 'Thou shalt commit adultery.'

Round and round Rotary press from 1825. The paper was pressed against the type as it rolled around the large roller. Ink was applied to the type by a roller, too, making the whole process run smoothly.

NOW JUMP TO... ◑ **PHOTOGRAPHY page 54;** ◑ **THE INTERNET page 128**

Rolling news Huge modern press using offset lithography to print The *Sun*. It can print, cut and arrange 20,000 complete newspapers every hour.

THE Sun

Saturday, February 22, 1455 · One farthing

JOB THREAT TO SCRIBES

THOUSANDS of scribes facing the axe last night were barred from protesting by a vow of silence.

Holy unnecessary . . . Sun scribes · *Monastery of Misery — Page 9*

boy . . . Gutenberg

ble's a oddle r me, laims venter

By PAIGE TURNER

NT guru Gutenberg aims to mass-duce books, start with the **BIBLE**.

reckons his s can churn out copies, each 2 pages long, ist three years. at's as long as would take a be to do **ONE**.

Gutenberg's be far cheaper.

s new press is likely to be in e demand ng pioneers of cultural "Renais-ce" in Europe. riters and art-are desperate drag us out of Dark Ages. And will be keen to ulate their ideas ly on paper.

e said: "I'm ing for ten per off if I bung regular work."

OWN YOUR OWN BOOK

PAGES 6-7

INKREDIBLE

Brilliant printing 'press' invention ends centuries of hand-drawn Sun

WELCOME to the new Sun — the first issue produced using a miraculous printing machine.

We have signed a deal with German inventor Johannes Gutenberg to use his state-of-the-art "press". It can produce dozens of copies a night.

You may not see any differ-

By HUGH LET-PACKARD

ence in quality — a tribute to our scribes who have hand-drawn the paper for millennia. They worked long into the night, hunched over their quills . . . but now face the boot.

Sun Backs Renaissance — Page 9

Im-press-ive . . . Gutenberg gizmo

1506 DA VINCI: CENTURIES AHEAD OF HIS TIME

LEONARDO da Vinci was arguably the greatest genius of all time. A brilliant artist, he was also a disciplined and extremely inquisitive scientist and inventor. Some of his visionary insights were 400 years ahead of their time.

Much of what we know about Leonardo's scientific ideas comes from his notebooks. He wrote about geometry, engineering, plants and animals, and physics; he made incredible anatomical drawings and designs for a huge number of innovative buildings and machines. Today, about 6,000 pages survive – less than half the original number.

Leonardo (1452–1519) famously penned his notes in mirror writing, but there is perhaps little intrigue in that – he was left-handed, and by jotting from right-to-left he avoided smudging his ink.

In the 1480s, while employed by the Duke of Milan, Leonardo began studying birds in great detail. He quickly realised they are

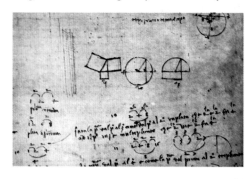

Maths problem Leonardo's mathematical notes. Maths was just about the only subject he couldn't do extremely well, although he saw its importance.

Grand designs Leonardo's plans for an aerial screw (above), drawn some time between 1483 and 1486. The model of Leonardo's aerial screw (left) was made in recent years.

built very differently from people, and that humans would never fly simply by using their arms alone to flap big wings. Around 1490, he drew plans for a flying machine with wings which flapped using the combined effort of arms and legs. Even this would not have worked, but it was an impressive idea.

During this same period, he also designed a parachute, a glider, a flying boat with wings and a large tail, and a kind of helicopter. In fact, the helicopter was an 'aerial screw'. It was designed to spin rapidly, pulling itself up into the air as a screw pulls itself into wood. It is one of Leonardo's most famous inventions. Others included a primitive tank, a multi-barrelled gun and an extraordinary programmable 'car'.

In 1501 Leonardo moved to Florence, rented a few rooms in a monastery and set up his studio. Their exact location was a mystery until researchers discovered them in 2005; some of Leonardo's paintings were still on the walls. It was probably in these rooms, in 1503, that he began one of the world's most famous paintings: the Mona Lisa. Experts believe the subject

MIND BOGGLER
● In 1994, Bill Gates bought one of Leonardo's notebooks, the Codex Leicester, for $30 million.

of this mysterious portrait was Lisa Gherardini the daughter of a silk merchant who lived close to the monastery.

Leonardo was born out of wedlock and was reputed to be a vegetarian homosexual pacifist, very unusual for his time. He lived in an era of phenomenal change normally called the Renaissance (rebirth), which ran from the 15th until the 17th century.

No one knows exactly how or when, but the Renaissance seems to have begun because rich people in Florence, Italy, became obsessed by the classical era – the time of Ancient Greek philosophers and scholars, and of the Roman Empire.

The Renaissance blew the cobwebs off the old but inspiring poetry, music, art, mathematics and science. Across much of Europe new books were written, with fresh ideas questioning the old assumptions.

Early in the 16th century, the Renaissance reached England. Here, the emphasis was more on literature and philosophy than art and architecture. William Shakespeare (1564–1616) was an English Renaissance man. So too was Francis Bacon (1561–1626), often credited with clearly defining the modern scientific method of observation and experimentation.

The da Vinci Code

The publication of Dan Brown's fictional novel *The Da Vinci Code* in 2000 – and the release of the film version in 2006 – brought Leonardo back into the public's consciousness again. In the story, Leonardo had been part of a powerful secret society called the Priory of Sion, and he had left clues in some of his greatest artworks.

Model of a machine Leonardo designed to grind curved mirrors.

WHAT IN THE WORLD?
1474 William Caxton prints the first book in English.
1480 The first playing cards with hearts-clubs-diamonds-spades originate in France.
1481 Spanish Inquisition begins, in which Spanish state and church finds and punishes heretics.
1485 The Battle of Bosworth Field, in Leicestershire, ends the War of the Roses.
1492 Christopher Columbus and his crew discover the 'New World', the Americas.

NOW JUMP TO... ● HELICOPTER page 104; ● POWERED FLIGHT page 84

THE Sun

sday, November 24, 1506 — 1½ farthings

EXCLUSIVE

My wife's such a Mona . . . I can't get her to smile!

ER FELLA OPENS HEART TO SUN: PAGE 5

: . . . was he dad?

crets dden' Jesus ainting

OU DICKRUS

IRACY theorists beside themlast night over alleged bloopers Vinci's Last mural. They d to know:

IY there is no e from which sciples drank.

IY the apostle ooks like a girl.

IY John, Peter esus appear to an "M" shape.

nut gasped: ecause John is ly Mary Magdaho was secretly nt by Jesus and is secretly for and there's no e because SHE Holy Grail and Jesus died she ly had his baby heir descendants ill alive and it's secret and Leonin on it."

al of Leo in-: "That's tosh."

DA VINCI CODE

CRACKED

Notebook scribbles are 'mirror' writing

He da man . . . genius Leonardo

By DEE TECTIVE, Investigations Editor

THE baffling scribbles in Leonardo da Vinci's notebooks can today be unmasked by The Sun . . . as MIRROR writing.

The Italian artist-cum-inventor, 48, was thought to have written his inspired musings in code to protect his ideas from thieves or even the Church. But we can reveal he simply writes them left-handed and from right to left.

Holding a mirror to them makes them instantly understandable . . . if you speak Italian.

Inside Da Mind of Da Vinci — Pages 4 & 5

● 25

INSIDE DA MIND OF DA VINCI

Genius plans 'tank', car and glider

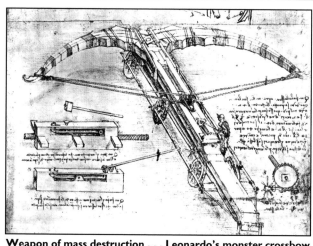

Weapon of mass destruction . . . Leonardo's monster crossbow

LEONARDO da Vinci has designed a chilling array of futuristic war machines which would terrorise an enemy — if we could ever build them.

They are contained within the 13,000 pages of his illustrations and notes in "mirror writing" which give a fascinating glimpse inside the mind of a great genius.

The Sun has engaged a team of craftsmen to build models of the Italian's inventions.

One is a tortoise-like armoured "tank" which would house eight men as they ploughed into the enemy. It is covered in metal plates and armed with several guns. Da Vinci has also invented a 76ft crossbow, firing a projectile huge enough

By IAN O'VATOR, Technology Correspondent

to cause panic. And he has drawn a fearsome gun which would fire from **TEN** barrels at once.

Ironically, da Vinci is **ANTI**-war. And his books are also crammed with a host of peaceful inventions. He has drawn several flying machines — and predicts man will one day take to the air.

Another brainwave is a spring-powered "robot car", which can propel itself for a short distance and even be programmed to steer.

Da Vinci (left) has also designed a boat that sails **UNDER** water and a cog-wheeled gizmo that may calculate large numbers. He has suggested mirrors be used to harness the sun's power to heat water.

But one sceptic said yesterday: "Look, Leonardo is a clever bloke and a great painter, but we just don't have the technology to build these things. Even if they work, some won't get made for centuries."

Turtle war . . . Leo reckons armoured 'tortoise' would be an amazing weapon

Firepower . . . Leonardo's ten-barrelled gun, and its sketch

Runabout . . . his programmable car is spring-powered

1610 GALILEO'S TELESCOPE REINVENTS ASTRONOMY

ITALIAN scientist Galileo Galilei was not the first person to claim Earth orbited the sun. But he was the first who could prove it. His observations made through a home-made telescope changed the course of science.

It is hard for anyone looking at the stars 'moving' across the heavens to accept that they are not revolving around Earth – and that our planet is itself rotating and hurtling through space. That is why 'geocentrism' – the mistaken belief that the Earth is at the centre of the universe – was accepted as fact for more than 1,000 years.

Galileo's observations, 1610.
These pages from *Sidereus Nuncius* show Galileo's observations of the craters on the moon.

Galileo's telescope, 161[0]
Replica of one of the earliest telescopes made by Galileo Galilei. It could produce magnification of around 20 times.

The motions of the sun, moon and other planets relative to the stars had to be explained too, however – and several geocentric theories were put forward. The most sophisticated was by Greco-Roman astronomer Ptolemy (Claudius Ptolemaeus, c. 120-180 BC), in the 2nd century BC. In the 'Ptolemaic system', the planets, the sun and the moon each occupied a separate rotating sphere around the Earth. In Europe and many parts of Asia, this was assumed correct for 1,400 years.

So compelling and deep-seated was the geocentric view that few people questioned it. Universities, run by the Catholic Church, adopted Ptolemy's system as fact. By the late Middle Ages, anyone who dared to suggest alternative views risked being declared a heretic.

However, several astronomers, even in ancient times, had put forward 'heliocentric' systems – with Earth and the other planets in orbit around a central sun. Most important was Polish astronomer Nicolaus Copernicus (1473–1543), whose influential work *De Revolutionibus Orbium Coelestium* ('On the Revolution of Celestial Spheres') was published in 1543.

His system found increasing support during the second half of the 16th century. German astronomer Johannes Kepler (1571–1630) developed it, using geometry to show how planetary orbits around the sun must be ellipses (flattened circles). But it was the publication of Galileo's observations that proved crucial in its acceptance.

In 1609 Galileo (1564–1642[)] heard about the telescope, invented b[y] Dutchman Hans Lippershey (1570–1619). H[e] had soon made his own, improved the desig[n] and turned it to the night sky. He observe[d] several things that backed 'Copernican' theor[y] – in particular, moons in orbit around Jupite[r]. Clearly, he thought, not everything revolve[d] around the Earth. He also saw that Venus ha[d] phases like those of the moon – that could onl[y] happen if it was moving around the sun. I[n] 1610 he published a small book called *Sidereu[s] Nuncius* (The Starry Messenger) in which h[e] explained his observations.

Galileo quickly became a champion o[f] the heliocentric view. He als[o] uncovered evidence against th[e] prevailing view that the heav[-] ens were perfect: craters on th[e] moon and spots on the sun.

At first, Galileo found favou[r] with high-ranking Churc[h] officials. But in later publica[-] tions he ridiculed the Church['s] teachings. He was commanded not to suppor[t] the heliocentric view. In 1633 he was calle[d] to Rome, where he faced the Inquisition. Hi[s] books were banned and he spent the rest of hi[s] days under house arrest.

In the 1680s, English scientist Isaac Newto[n] showed how gravitational forces could explai[n] the planets' orbits around the sun. His Law o[f] Gravitation gave mathematical support to the heliocentric view. At last, astronomers coul[d] use equations to predict the motions of the planets – in their orbits around the sun – wit[h] unprecedented accuracy.

MIND BOGGLER

- It took until 1758 for the Catholic Church to allow the heliocentric theory to be taught. And it took until 1992 before Galileo received a posthumous apology from Pope John Paul II over his treatment.

The Ptolemaic system, from *Margarita Philosophica*, 1535.
Illustration showing the Ptolemeic system of concentric spheres. The Earth – and humankind – is in the centre.

WHAT IN THE WORLD?

1514   The mathematical symbols + and − first used, in Holland.

1522   Portuguese sailors complete the first circumnavigation of the globe.

1535   The first modern diving bell; an earlier form is described by Aristotle (384–322 BC).

1543   Flemish anatomist Andreas Vesalius (1514–1564) publishes his book *De Humanis Corporis Fabrica* (On the Working of the Human Body).

1543   Polish astronomer Nicolaus Copernicus publishes *De Revolutionibus Orbium Coelestium* (On the revolution of celestial spheres).

1556   The worst earthquake in history hits China, killing 830,000 people.

1588   Francis Drake (c. 1540–1596) beats the Spanish Armada.

1592   Galileo invents the thermoscope, the predecessor of the thermometer; it is primitive and inaccurate.

1605   Guy Fawkes' (1570–1606) Gunpowder Plot is foiled.

NOW JUMP TO... ◆ URANUS page 42; ◆ THE GALAXY page 92; ◆ MARS PROBES page 120

Johannes Kepler's model of the Universe
from *Mysterium Cosmographicum* (*Cosmic Mystery*) published in 1619 – with the sun at the centre. Kepler believed that planetary orbits were based on the 'Platonic solids', perfect geometrical forms.

EARTH REVOLVES AROUND

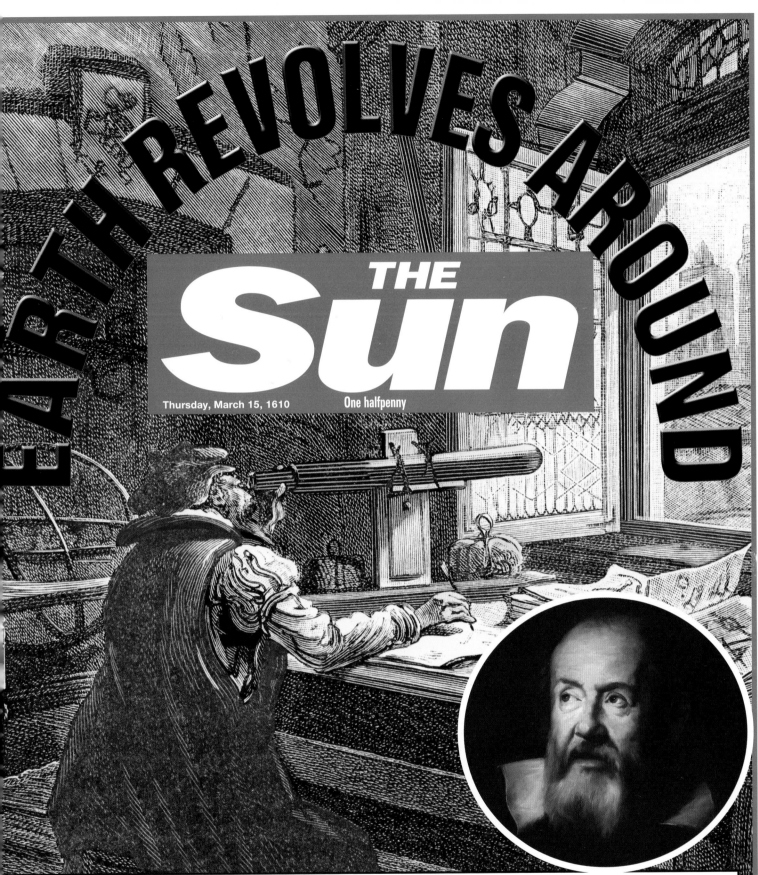

THE Sun

Thursday, March 15, 1610 — One halfpenny

. . . says Galileo, only bloke with a telescope

By **TERRY SCOPE** and **UNA VERSE,** Sun Reporters

EARTH revolves around the sun — **NOT** the other way round, The Sun can reveal.

The ground-breaking discovery was confirmed by astronomer Galileo Galilei, one of the world's only people with a telescope.

Galileo, 45, *(inset)* of Pisa, Italy, also says the moon has craters and mountains, the Milky Way is a colossal number of stars — and the sun has **SPOTS.** His findings, to be published in a book called The Starry Messenger, will outrage other scientists and religious leaders, who hate any suggestion that Earth is not the centre of everything.

MORE HEAVENLY BODIES: SEE PAGE THREE

1628 A MILESTONE IN THE STUDY OF ANATOMY

THE CIRCULATION of blood from the heart through arteries and back through veins may seem trivial and obvious now, but William Harvey's discovery during the 17th century was remarkable because it was at odds with the accepted view of anatomy. It was a major milestone on the long road to understanding the human body.

After graduating from Cambridge University, Harvey (1578–1657) studied medicine at the University of Padua, Italy, one of Europe's best medical schools at the time. He returned to England to be a doctor and became fascinated by the function of the blood and the way it moves through the body. He worked out that the heart pumps more blood every half hour than all the blood the body contains. This could only be explained by blood circulating.

What Harvey could not work out was how blood made its way from the ends of the arteries to the beginning of the veins, the start of its journey back to the heart. The arteries just keep on dividing, getting smaller and apparently disappearing into flesh. This makes Harvey's continued conviction about the idea of circulation even more amazing.

At the time, understanding of anatomy was rapidly advancing. The Flemish anatomist Andreas Vesalius (1514–1564) had stepped up the pace almost a century earlier. Also a graduate of Padua University, he had begun a revolution in thinking about the human body with his book *De Humani Corporis Fabrica* (On the Fabric of the Human Body) in 1543.

At the time European ideas about the body were dominated by the teachings of an ancient Greek physician called Galen, full name Claudius Galenus (129–200). He made major contributions to the science of anatomy and was revolutionary in his own day. As a physician, he attempted brain surgery, removed cataracts and promoted the patient-centred approach of Hippocrates (c. 460–377 BC).

Old view This illustration of the nervous system from the 15th century highlights the lack of detail in anatomical studies before Vesalius.

Picture this The human blood vessels, taken from Vesalius' book. The book's illustrations were by Jan Stephen Calcar (c. 1499–1546), a pupil of the famous painter Titian.

Galen discovered the basic functions of many systems within the body, including the kidney and the nervous system.

But many of his ideas were mistaken, partly because he carried out his research on animals – pigs, apes and goats. Galen thought blood ebbed and flowed like ocean tides – out and back through the same blood vessels. When the blood returned to the heart, it rid itself of impurities.

The pioneering work of Vesalius and Harvey encouraged fellow anatomists to re-evaluate the function of other human organs. The introduction of the microscope in the 1620s gave access to the body at a new and daunting level of detail. One of the pioneers of microscopic anatomy was Italian Marcello Malpighi (1628–1694), who discovered the existence of capillaries, the tiny blood vessels that complete the circuit between arteries and veins. Sadly for Harvey, the much-respected personal physician to Kings James I and Charles I, the discovery came four years after his own heart stopped pumping.

Calculating clock

German inventor Wilhelm Schickard (1592–1635) invented a mechanical calculator, which his contemporaries called the 'calculating clock'. He used it for working out astronomical tables – lists of figures predicting the positions of the sun, moon and planets in the sky. Schickard's designs were lost after his death, and were only rediscovered in the 20th century. A working replica of Schickard's device was built in 1960.

WHAT IN THE WORLD?

1615 Dutch settle on Manhattan Island, later New Amsterdam, now New York.
1617 Scottish mathematician John Napier devises a calculating device for multiplication, known as Napier's Bones.
1618 The beginning of the 30 Years' War in Europe.
1620 Dutch inventor Cornelius Drebbel builds an early submarine.
1620 The first modern violin is made.
1626 English philosopher Francis Bacon dies after stuffing a chicken with snow in a frozen food experiment.
1627 Francis Bacon's book *The New Atlantis* is published, predicting a host of inventions including telephones,
1621 Englishman William Oughtred invents the slide rule (a calculating device).

MIND BOGGLER
● The adult human body contains about seven litres of blood. Each litre contains four to five trillion red blood cells and six billion white blood cells.

Inside story Andreas Vesalius dissecting the forearm muscles of a cadaver, from his influential book *De Humani Corporis Fabrica* (On the Fabric of the Human Body).

Teaching tool 17th century wooden models used to teach anatomy and medicine. The rise of dissection in the 16th century had made models like these commonplace and more accurate.

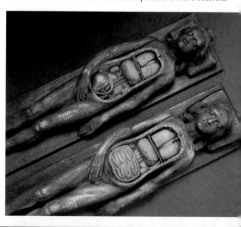

NOW JUMP TO... ❯ **MICROSCOPES page 32;** ❯ **VACCINATION page 46**

us . . . 'calculator'

ch yer pacus!

adget lds up h turn a rod

RRY THMETICK

CHINE that can
d subtract has
invented, The
n reveal.

s the first
nical "calcula-
- and has been
the "calculat-
ck" by its inven-
helm Schickard.

er device can
ached to it —
pgrade" which
s it to multiply
vide too.

Forget

gizmo has rotat-
s with numbers
ed on them.
move the rods
splay the results.

deal with num-
p to six digits
nd rings a bell
solution has
han six.

kard, a 36-year-
rman astronomy
sor, plans to use
vice to calculate
zing tables.

teacher said:
till kids get
ands on one —
forget how to
in their head."

MES ABLES FULL OUT INSIDE

BLOODY MARVEL

Heart pumps red fluid around our bodies – top doc

By ANNE EEMICK

THE heart pumps blood round
our bodies, the King's doctor
has sensationally discovered.

William Harvey's claim shat-
ters 1,400 years of established
thought on veins and arteries.

It was always believed blood ebbs
and flows like the tide, due to arteries contracting. But Harvey, 50, says
it leaves the heart, circulates round
us, then re-enters the pumping organ.

Beat That — Pages 6 & 7

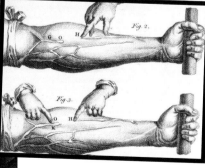

What's up, doc . . . Harvey shows off his findings to his friend King Charles last night. Above, sketches of veins in book he has written

● 31

1676 MICROSCOPE FINDS WHOLE NEW WORLD

THE DISCOVERY by Anton van Leeuwenhoek of tiny creatures living in pond water stunned the scientific world. Its importance was quickly realised, as was that of the microscope, which has literally given humanity a new view of the world.

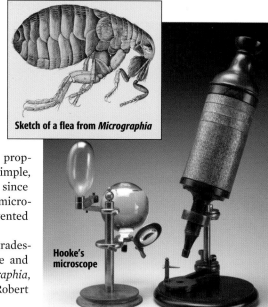
Sketch of a flea from *Micrographia*

People had known of the magnifying properties of lenses since ancient times. Simple, single-lens microscopes had been in use since the early 16th century and compound microscopes, with more than one lens, were invented around 1590.

Leeuwenhoek, a Dutch scientist and tradesman (1632–1723), was inspired to make and use them by a best-selling book, *Micrographia*, produced in 1665 by English scientist Robert Hooke (1635–1703).

It contained Hooke's stunning illustrations of a variety of magnified specimens, including woven cloth, a fly's eye, human hair and a flea enlarged to 45cm (18 inches) across.

Leeuwenhoek made a variety of microscopes by grinding his own lenses. Some could magnify by a factor of 270. He noticed tiny single-cell creatures in pond water and called them 'animalcules'. Nowadays we call them micro-organisms.

Leeuwenhoek – since dubbed the 'Father of Microbiology' –

Hooke's microscope

Compound microscope This is how most people think of microscopes: a barrel, with a lens at the top (the eyepiece) and a lens at the bottom (the objective). This one was made and used by Robert Hooke. He used it when he was putting together his book *Micrographia* (1665). Modern optical microscopes have a cluster of lenses at the eyepiece and the objective ends. The device on the left focuses light from an oil lamp onto the sample.

Leeuwenhoek's simple microscope Anton van Leeuwenhoek made hundreds of single-lens microscopes like this one. The specimen was placed on the tiny metal spike positioned at the focal point of the lens.

MIND BOGGLER
● Some water purifiers used by campers include a very fine filter with holes about one-thousandth of a millimetre in diameter. The filter traps single-celled organisms, such as bacteria and protozoa.

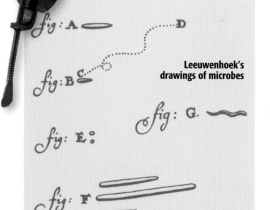
Leeuwenhoek's drawings of microbes

also observed bacteria and sperm.

Microscopes at that time produced distorted images at high magnification. Later 19th century microscopes produced clear images at very high magnifications by improving the manufacture of lenses and combining several at once. This new generation of instruments could probe inside cells, revealing a host of tiny structures.

In the 1870s, German physicist Ernst Abbe (1840–1905) realised there is a limit to the magnification of an optical microscope (one that uses light) – it cannot 'see' objects less than two thousandths of a millimetre across. Scientists found a way around this, by using a beam of electrons to illuminate the specimens – the electron microscope was invented in 1933. Electron microscopes, which produce images on a television screen, revolutionised the study of biology just as their predecessors had done.

In 1981, researchers at the computing firm IBM invented a new kind of microscope, the scanning tunnelling microscope. This does not produce images using light or electrons. Instead, it has a tiny probe that 'feels' its way across the surface of a specimen, following the

NOW JUMP TO... ◀ ANATOMY page 30; ▶ PASTEUR page 66

WHAT IN THE WORLD?

1643 Italian physicist Evangelista Torricelli (1608–1647) invents the mercury barometer.
1632 Galileo's *Dialogue Concerning Two World Views* challenges the ideas of force and motion handed down by the ancients.
1633 Bananas on sale in London.
1642 English Civil War starts.
1648 End of the Thirty Years' War in Europe.
1650 German inventor Otto von Guericke (1602–1686) makes a powerful vacuum pump.
1660 Samuel Pepys starts writing his famous diaries of London life.
1661 Anglo-Irish physicist Robert Boyle publishes *The Sceptical Chymist.*
1662 Boyle's law describing the behaviour of gases.
1663 King Charles II gives a royal charter to The Royal Society for the Advancement of Natural Knowledge (the Royal Society).
1665 English scientist Robert Hooke publishes *Micrographia.*
1666 The Great Fire of London.

Royal Observatory, Greenwich

Kings and queens have long had a fascination with the stars and planets – although they were often more interested in astrology than astronomy. With royal interest comes royal money, and until the 19th century, several important observatories were funded by royalty.

The Royal Observatory, Greenwich, was never used for astrology. Its main purpose was to prepare detailed tables of information regarding the positions and movements of the stars and planets. These tables, it was hoped, would help people to determine their position better at sea.

incredibly minute lumps and bumps formed by the atoms themselves. The image has to be visualised by a computer.

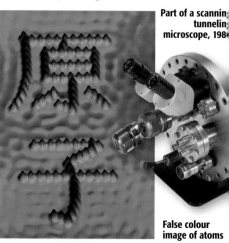
Part of a scanning tunnelling microscope, 198

False colour image of atoms

Atomic view The eyepieces on this scanning tunnelling microscope are only to help users position the specimen correctly. The probe inside this microscope can move atoms around; the picture shown here reads 'atom' in Japanese Kanji. It is 'written' in iron atoms on a copper surface.

THE Sun

Three farthings

esday, October 10, 1676

King's HQ for stargazing launched

By LUKE UPP

THE enormous new observatory for stargazers in South-East London was up and running last night.

John Flamsteed, appointed by King Charles last year as the first Astronomer Royal, has moved in.

The Greenwich building was designed by top architect Sir Christopher Wren.

The King (left) is hoping that greater study of the stars will lead to an improved method of navigating at sea.

Watch This Space — Page 2

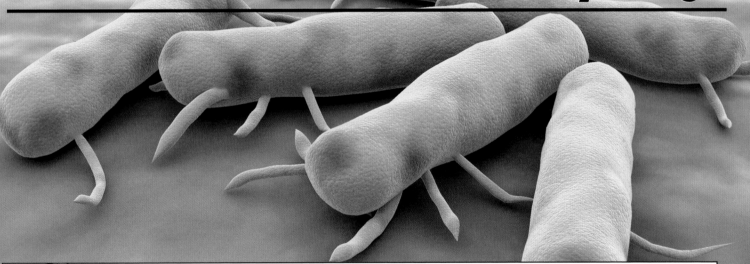

YUCK!

World is riddled with tiny bugs

THE entire planet is infested with disgusting little bugs invisible to the naked eye, The Sun can reveal.

The stomach-churning creepy-crawlies were found by a scientist using a microscope he made.

His horrific findings have been

By MIKE ROBE and ANNA MEBA

sent to London's new Royal Society. Anton van Leeuwenhoek *(left)*, from Amsterdam, Holland, calls the creatures *(above)* "animalcules". Chillingly, he insists they are **EVERYWHERE**.

Leeuwenhoek, 44, said: "They are incredibly small, nay so small, in my sight, that I judged that even if 100 of

these wee animals lay stretched out one against another, they could not reach the length of a grain of sand.

"I saw, with great wonder, that there were many very little living animalcules, very prettily a-moving. The biggest shot through water like a pike."

Health bosses are forming an emergency plan and urged the public not to panic. A source said: "We face a lifetime of scrubbing. It's that simple."

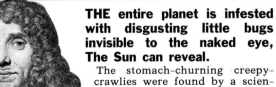

SOAP: OUR ONLY HOPE

PAGES 2,3, 4&5

● 33

1705 SIR ISAAC NEWTON, SCIENTIST SUPREME

ALMOST 300 years after his death, Sir Isaac Newton is still a household name thanks to his ground-breaking theories on gravity and motion which explain the movement of most objects under everyday conditions.

Newton (1642–1727), born in a tiny Lincolnshire village, was the best-known physicist and mathematician of his day.

He began his university education in 1661 at Trinity College, Cambridge, when the ancient ideas of the Greek philosopher Aristotle (384–322 BC) still held sway.

Some scientists had begun to overturn those long-standing notions. By the time Newton went to college, many were convinced matter was made of tiny particles and that Earth and other planets orbit the sun – the 'heliocentric' theory. Newton learned about these ideas and filled his notebooks with 'philosophical questions', which he would follow up later.

In 1665, the university was closed for 18 months when plague broke out in London. Newton went to stay at his mother's house in Lincolnshire and there, still in his mid-20s, he made most of his important discoveries.

In a darkened room, Newton passed sunlight through glass prisms and lenses. For hundreds of years, people had seen the result of this – a spectrum of all the colours of the rainbow

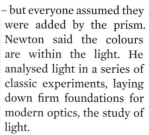

Coloured view White light – a mixture of colours.

MIND BOGGLER
● A descendant of the tree under which Newton was sitting when he had his gravity revelation is planted outside the room in which he studied at Cambridge University.

– but everyone assumed they were added by the prism. Newton said the colours are within the light. He analysed light in a series of classic experiments, laying down firm foundations for modern optics, the study of light.

It is said that while doing this he invented the cat flap to avoid being disturbed by his pet's comings and goings. There is no proof of this story – but it has been in circulation for decades.

Another, more likely, story is that Newton had his famous revelation about gravity while sitting under an apple tree at his mother's house. He realised that the same force of gravity that causes apples to fall to the ground applies at much greater distances. He realised it also pulled the moon towards Earth, keeping it in our orbit. By extending the same argument to the sun and the planets, Newton could see that gravity was a universal force responsible for keeping planets in their orbits, backing the heliocentric theory.

Newton is equally well-known for his three laws of motion, which use mathematics to describe the way objects move. They are simple, but not obvious. For example, the first law says a moving object will carry on moving forever unless a force acts on it. That is not our experience of everyday life – but only because friction is the force that slows objects down. Aristotle had wrongly said things stop moving unless there is a force to keep them moving, which is the common sense view.

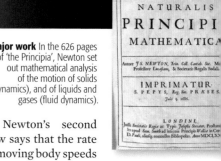

Major work In the 626 pages of 'the Principia', Newton set out mathematical analysis of the motion of solids (dynamics), and of liquids and gases (fluid dynamics).

Newton's second law says that the rate a moving body speeds up or down is proportional to the force acting on it. The third law says that for every 'action – or force applied to a body – there is an equal and opposite reaction.

He published his discoveries about motion and gravity in 1687, in perhaps the most important scientific book of all time: *Philosophiae Naturalis Principia Mathematica* (Mathematical Principles of Natural Philosophy). It brought him great acclaim in Britain and across Europe His second most important book, *Opticks*, was published in 1704; it contained his discoveries about light.

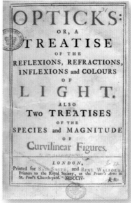

Light reading In 1704, Newton published his collected research on light and colour.

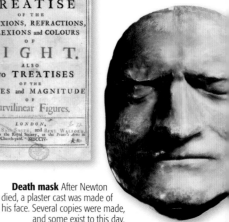

Death mask After Newton died, a plaster cast was made of his face. Several copies were made, and some exist to this day.

NOW JUMP TO... ● GALILEO page 28; ● EINSTEIN page 88; ● MOON LANDINGS page 118

THE Sun

Thursday, February 15, 1705 · Three farthings

HE ALSO 'FOUND' GRAVITY
PAGES 4 & 5

Cat flap genius knighted

HE'S SIR ISAAC

EXCLUSIVE by LAURA MOTION

ISAAC Newton, the egghead behind the cat-flap, is to be knighted, it was announced last night.

Newton, 62, currently crime-busting boss of the Royal Mint, will become Sir this year.

His ingenious flap *(right),* which enables moggies to come and go as they please, has proved the pivotal moment in a lifetime of invention.

Newton *(left)* also devised a few laws of motion, toyed with lenses and discovered that gravity is a force throughout the universe, affecting every particle of matter.

But a Government spokesman said: "Look, apples fall on the ground. So what? The cat-flap was pure genius. That will prove his lasting legacy."

KNIGHTHOOD JOY

By DEE PRESSION
and TERRY BULLRAGE

ISAAC Newton's pals were yesterday hoping his knighthood will bring him joy at last — and end the rages, feuds and nervous breakdowns which have plagued his life.

Highly-strung Newton, 62, has long had an appalling temper and flies off the handle if rival boffins dare to make the slightest criticism of his work.

Friends are praying the gong from Queen Anne will give him the recognition he deserves, though it is more for his talent at nailing forgers as Head of the Royal Mint than for his scientific genius.

Newton's great triumph was, of course, the cat flap which he invented to avoid having to let his moggie in or out as he concentrated on experiments with light and lenses.

Orb

But scientists reckon the life-long bachelor's 1687 law of "gravity", inspired by watching an **APPLE** fall from a tree in his mum's Lincolnshire garden, could be almost as big.

Newton, then a Cambridge University maths professor, worked out that what made the fruit fall to the ground was the same force as the one which keeps the moon orbiting Earth. He even proved it mathematically — and went on to say gravity affects every single particle in the universe.

His biographer John Conduitt said: "It came into his thought that the power of gravity must extend much further than was usually thought. Why not as high as the moon, said he to himself, and if so, that must influence her motion and perhaps retain her in her orbit."

Newton said: "I thereby compared the force requisite to keep the moon in her orb with force of gravity at the surface of the Earth — and found them answer pretty nearly."

He revealed this "law of universal gravitation" in his hit book Philosophiae Naturalis Principia Mathematica, which also contains his legendary three laws of motion.

The Prof had already made stunning breakthroughs in the study of light, using a prism to show how it is made up of different colours. He even built the world's first reflecting telescope, far better than earlier ones which produced so many coloured beams they were unable to give a clear image.

Newton is now Head of the Mint on a staggering £2,000 a year — and has had several counterfeiters hanged for making dud coins. Friends say the crime-busting is an outlet for his rage, said to have been sparked by his dad dying before he was born and his mum then abandoning him with his gran for nine years after she remarried.

Once, he threatened to torch the house his mum and step-dad live in — with them in it.

But a pal said last night: "He loves hunting down these forgers. Maybe the knighthood will cheer him up too."

Scope for improvement . . . Newton's reflecting telescope knocks spots off older 'refracting' ones

APPLEY

EVER AFTER

1752 ELECTRICITY AND MAGNETISM

BENJAMIN Franklin was a multi-talented man, famous for many things – perhaps most of all the kite experiment he devised to prove for the first time that lightning is electricity.

Born in Boston, Franklin (1706–1790) was an inventor, philosopher, musician and statesman. He was one of the Founding Fathers of the United States and signed both the Declaration of Independence and the Constitution.

His kite experiment did not involve simply directing a lightning bolt down the string, which would almost certainly have killed him. Instead he used the kite to draw charge from the bottom of a thundercloud. Then he placed his knuckle on a metal door-key he had run up the string – and felt a spark.

Making magnets A page from William Gilbert's *De Magnete*, showing one process for making artificial magnets – by lining up hot steel north-south and beating it as it cools. **Left:** William Gilbert.

As a result of his interest in electricity, Franklin invented the lightning rod, which protects buildings by conducting charge from thunderclouds safely to the ground.

But Franklin's experiment with electricity was by no means the first. In fact the strange, invisible forces of electricity and magnetism had been known since ancient times.

Many materials become 'electrically charged' when rubbed together, and several minerals are naturally magnetic. The Chinese had been using one of these, magnetite, in compasses from the 4th century or earlier.

Umbrella man

Jonas Hanway (1712–1786) was the first man in London to carry an umbrella, despite them being all the rage in Paris at the time. Collapsible umbrellas similar to modern umbrellas have been used in China for 1,700 years.

The first person to investigate magnetism and electricity scientifically was William Gilbert (1544–1603), personal doctor to Queen Elizabeth I. His book *De Magnete* (On Magnets), published in 1600, described how he made a magnetised model of Earth. Like any magnet, it had a north and south pole, and when Gilbert moved a magnetic compass around his 'Earth' it always pointed to the poles – as a real compass does on the real Earth.

Gilbert suggested magnetism keeps Earth and the other planets in orbit around the sun. Nearly 80 years later, German physicist Otto von Guericke (1602–1686) said he thought electricity was responsible. In 1687, Isaac Newton (1642–1727) used his laws of motion to show how the mysterious force 'gravity' provided a mathematical explanation.

Von Guericke made the first machine to produce constant electric charge – a friction generator. It was a ball of sulphur mounted on a spindle, with a handle to make it spin. Touching the ball as it rotated charged it – and whatever you touched it with – with electricity. In the early 18th century, this became the standard way to produce electricity for experiments, though the sulphur ball was replaced with a glass one.

In 1745, German clergyman Ewald von Kleist (c. 1700–1748) discovered a way to store charge produced by friction generators. Around the same time, Dutch physicist Pieter van Musschenbroek (1692-1761) invented the

same thing. The device is called the Leyden Jar, after his home town.

The 18th century was the heyday of experiments with static electricity. Most scientists assumed electricity and magnetism were invisible weightless 'fluids'. The word 'charged' was first used at this time, to mean filled-up – i.e. with electrical 'fluid'.

We now know that electricity is a property inherent in some subatomic particles.

Storage jar A Leyden Jar used in the 1740s: a glass jar, foil-coated inside and out, and normally water-filled. By connecting a static electricity generator to the metal knob, a large amount of electrical energy can be stored, and used for experiments. **Above:** Pieter van Musschenbroek, one of the inventors of the Leyden Jar.

WHAT IN THE WORLD?

1705 English scientist Francis Hauksbee (1666–1713) proves that sound cannot travel through a vacuum.

1705 English scientist Edmund Halley (1656–1742) correctly predicts the return of a comet in 1758 – it will eventually become known as Halley's comet.

1707 The Act of Union unites England and Scotland.

1709 English entrepreneur Abraham Darby (c. 1678–1717) pioneers the use of coke in the smelting of iron, at Coalbrookdale.

1714 Gabriel Fahrenheit invents the temperature scale named after him.

1714 British government offers a £20,000 prize for determining a ship's longitude at sea.

1721 Robert Walpole becomes the first British Prime Minister.

1730 The sextant, a navigational instrument, is invented independently in Britain and America.

1746 The first mention of Yorkshire pudding.

1748 Ruins of volcano-hit Pompeii are discovered.

NOW JUMP TO... ◆ BATTERIES, page 48; ◆ ELECTRIC MACHINES, page 50

Glass generator Glass frictional generator made by Francis Hauksbee (1666–1713), curato of experiments at th Royal Society.

THE Sun

Three farthings

Wednesday, June 16, 1752

SHOCK & AWE

Strike a kite... Ben's perilous experiment

silly . . hit in France

London oddball taunted for using umbrella

PETER PATTER
RAINE DROPPE

ADVENTURER Jonas Hanway braves ridicule wherever he goes for carrying an UMBRELLA in London.

The barmy device, a kind of portable, hand-held roof, originated in the Far East as a shelter from the sun.

It has become popular in Paris to keep rain off too.

Londoners find the contraption ludicrous, partly BECAUSE it is popular in France.

But Hanway, 50, famous for his travels in Russia, Germany and England, insists it will catch on here once people get over their silliness about using the device.

He says he is determined to carry an umbrella to the end of his days, despite constant taunts of "Frenchman, French-man" and repeated soaking from passing carriage drivers.

Dry Again — Page 7

Franklin's kite proves lightning IS electricity

A TOP inventor has proved lightning is electricity — by flying a kite in a storm.

Benjamin Franklin, 46, a famous American intellectual, extracted sparks from a cloud in Philadelphia yesterday.

By IAN CLEMENT and CLAUD BURST

The "electrical fire" ran down the kite string and Franklin was able to collect the charge.

The experiment was highly dangerous. Franklin is said to have felt "exquisite pleasure" at its success.

On Cloud Nine — Pages 6 & 7

● **39**

1761 THE PROBLEM OF LONGITUDE

ACCURATE navigation at sea became a huge and sometimes deadly problem as long-distance voyages grew more common in the 17th century. Determining a ship's longitude was the major difficulty – one which John Harrison, a self-taught British clockmaker, ingeniously solved.

Every point on Earth has a unique combination of latitude and longitude. Latitude is distance north or south of the equator. Longitude is distance east or west of the 0° line of longitude at Greenwich, London. A sailor navigating his way across an ocean needs to know both measurements to work out his exact position.

Latitude can be determined easily using the stars or the sun. Longitude was more troublesome. As one travels east or west, the time of day changes – this is the principle behind time zones. The time at 90 degrees west is six hours behind Greenwich, for example. So a sailor who left Britain with a clock showing the time at Greenwich would be able to tell his longitude by comparing Greenwich time with local time on the ship, which could be determined from the sun's height in the sky. But the only clocks that were accurate enough

Line of latitude

Line of longitude

Old timepiece Detail of the Wells Cathedral Clock (1392), the second oldest surviving clock in the world, and part of the Science Museum's collection.

over the long period of a sea voyage used pendulums, which are no use on a ship due to the rocking motion and extreme fluctuations in temperature.

On dry land, pendulum clocks, first built by Dutch scientist Christiaan Huygens (1629–1695) in 1656, kept much better time than their predecessors. But swings in temperature made the pendulums expand and contract, so the clocks would gain or lose a few seconds per day. In 1727 Harrison (1693–1776) invented the gridiron pendulum, whose length never changed thanks to a clever arrangement of different metals whose expansions cancelled each other out. It was far more accurate than its rivals. But it would still be no use at sea because of its vulnerability to motion.

So Harrison, in an attempt to win the Government's substantial Longitude Prize, built three spring-driven clocks, each more accurate and reliable than the last. The 'marine chronometer' which won him the prize was a portable watch. During a four-month voyage to Jamaica in 1761-1762 it lost only five seconds.

Marine chronometers remained an essential part of long-distance

Never built Galileo was the first person to design a pendulum clock – but he never built it. This model of his design was made in the 19th century.

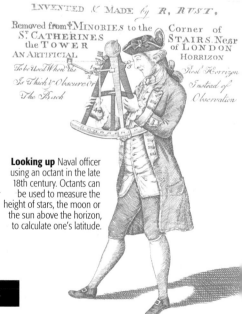

Mariner's compass, 1770s By measuring speed and direction, a mariner can set and follow a course. A compass helps with direction, but nautical speed was always a problem.

WHAT IN THE WORLD?

1755 Huge earthquake in Lisbon kills nearly 100,000 people.

1765 John Montagu (1718–1792), 4th Earl of Sandwich invents a new snack – the sandwich.

1757 The beginning of British rule in India.

1758 A commission in Britain sets the 'Imperial' standards of measurement.

1760 Benjamin Franklin (1706–1790) installs the first ever lightning rods, in Philadelphia.

MIND BOGGLER

● Modern GPS systems can determine your position to within two metres. In the future, accuracy could improve to about one centimetre.

navigation until the introduction of navigational radio beacons in the 1930s. Today, navigation is much easier thanks to cheap and accurate GPS (Global Positioning System) receivers, which can determine someone's position to within a few metres anywhere on Earth.

But even a modern GPS relies on clocks: without a highly accurate atomic clock in each of the satellites involved in the system, it would be useless.

Looking up Naval officer using an octant in the late 18th century. Octants can be used to measure the height of stars, the moon or the sun above the horizon, to calculate one's latitude.

NOW JUMP TO... ● BRUNEL page 62; ● MOTOR CAR page 74; ● POWERED FLIGHT page 84

HERO OF THE HOUR

Clock genius makes sailing safe

Ahead of his time... Harrison with his superb chronometer

A CLOCKMAKER has made sailing safe — by inventing a watch that keeps amazing time at sea.

John Harrison's ingenious "chronometer" contains springs and

EXCLUSIVE by IONA ROLEX

tiny beams to resist the rocking motion and temperature changes on a ship which make pendulum clocks useless.

It means navigators can now determine their position on a map almost

exactly using the relationship between longitude and time. They keep Greenwich time on the watch and work out local time from the sun's position.

Harrison's watch has just been tested on a voyage to Jamaica — and the calculation of the ship's position on arrival was only **TWO**

MILES out. Harrison, 68, has ended the guesswork of "dead reckoning" which destroyed so many ships.

One Navy chief said: "I'm amazed. I thought it was all a wind-up."

Now Harrison is set to trouser a massive £20,000 prize the Government offered after the wrecking

of our fleet in 1707. Some 800 men died when the ships hit rocks and sank off the Scilly Isles.

The catastrophe prompted the Longitude Act, which offered the cash for the first person to devise a more accurate way to work out a ship's position.

All Hands On Deck — Page 5

● 41

1781 HERSCHEL: A GOLDEN AGE OF ASTRONOMY

Planet man William Herschel, who discovered the planet Uranus. He also made an extensive star catalogue of the northern sky and discovered infrared radiation.

URANUS was the first new planet found since ancient times – and William Herschel's momentous discovery ushered in a golden age of astronomy.

Aside from the sun, the ancients picked out six objects that shift their position night-by-night relative to the 'fixed' stars: the moon, Mercury, Venus, Mars, Jupiter and Saturn. Uranus is very difficult to see with the naked eye, and moves more slowly across the sky than the other planets, so ancient astronomers did not recognise it as a planet.

That all changed with the advent of the telescope.

William Herschel (1738 – 1822) – born in Hanover, Germany – moved to England at 19. He was an accomplished musician and composer but became fascinated by astronomy. He built about 400 telescopes altogether, including the one with which he discovered Uranus in 1781.

Herschel was keen to name it Georgium Sidus (George's Star) in honour of King George III, who was ruler of Hanover too. Other astronomers – particularly those abroad – were not happy with the name and for several decades the planet was generally referred to as 'Herschel'. By the 1820s, the name Uranus was widely accepted.

Herschel made his momentous discovery with a reflecting telescope – one with a mirror to collect and focus light from dim and distant objects in space. The biggest telescope Herschel made was 40 feet (12 metres) long,

NOW JUMP TO... ◐ GALILEO page 28; ➜ SPACE PROBES page 120

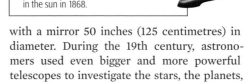

Light study When attached to a telescope, this 19th century spectroscope helped astronomers analyse the light from stars and planets. Norman Lockyer used it to discover helium in the sun in 1868.

with a mirror 50 inches (125 centimetres) in diameter. During the 19th century, astronomers used even bigger and more powerful telescopes to investigate the stars, the planets, the sun and moon.

The 19th century saw many astronomical breakthroughs. In 1838, German mathematician Friedrich Bessel (1784–1846) became the first person to work out the distance to a star. From the 1840s, astronomers used photography to capture beautiful images of dim and distant objects. And in the 1860s, scientists used a technique called spectroscopy to work out the chemical composition of the sun and stars. In 1868, Norman Lockyer (1836–1920) discovered an element not known on Earth. He called it 'helium', after the Greek word for the sun, *helios*. Helium was isolated in a laboratory in 1895.

MIND BOGGLER

● Uranus takes just over 84 Earth years to complete each orbit around the sun.

WHAT IN THE WORLD?

1765 James Watt (1736–1819) improves the design of the steam engine, by inventing the separate condenser.

1774 Hypnotism is used for the first time to treat disease, by German doctor Franz Mesmer (1734–1815).

1776 The first of James Watt's steam engines is installed.

1776 The American colonies declare independence.

1778 Antoine Lavoisier (1743–1794) discovers that air is made largely of two gases (oxygen and nitrogen), and that oxygen is responsible for the process of combustion.

1779 Dutch scientist Jan Ingenhousz (1730–1799) discovers photosynthesis in plants.

1779 English entrepreneur Abraham Darby III (1750–1791) completes the first iron bridge, at Coalbrookdale in England.

Like clockwork This orrery, made shortly after the discovery of Uranus, shows the seven planets in orbit around the sun.

The mathematics of astronomy became more sophisticated during the 19th century, too. By working out the orbit of Uranus very accurately, astronomers could tell that there must be another planet whose gravitational influence was disturbing the path of Uranus through space. This planet was Neptune and it was first sighted in 1846 – exactly where calculations had predicted it would be.

I don't believe it

No one has ever really spotted William Shakespeare in the night sky, as the *Sun* story opposite suggests – but they probably could. Up to 5,000 stars are visible to the naked eye at any one time on a clear, dark night – they are arranged randomly, of course, and an infinite number of different pictures could be drawn by playing dot-to-dot.

In ancient times, astronomers saw mythical creatures, everyday objects and gods in the night sky – patterns called constellations. Nowadays, constellations are simply regions of the sky, which are useful for describing where to find astronomical objects. They are still called by their old Latin names, such as Ursa Major, the Great Bear and Orion, the Hunter.

In 2005, just for fun, astronomers identified a new constellation – a group of stars that look just like the television character Victor Meldrew, played by actor Richard Wilson. The *Sun* carried the story on its front page.

Reflection The Great Rosse Telescope, at Birr Castle in Ireland, was the largest in the world from 1845 to 1917. Its mirror was 72 inches (184 centimetres) in diameter.

THE Sun

day, April 27, 1781 — Three farthings

Bard found in space

ASTRONOMERS have found a group of stars which look just like William Shakespeare. The outline of Britain's greatest playwright was spotted after stargazers spent many, many hours staring into space. One said: "It's simply incredible. Look, there he is." But one rival astronomer sniped: "I don't believe it. There is an infinite number of stars. Look hard enough and you'll find anyone. Falstaff even."

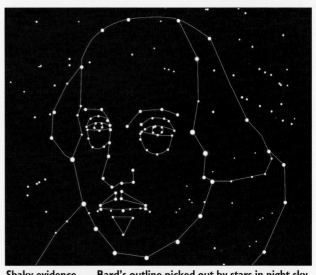

Shaky evidence . . . Bard's outline picked out by stars in night sky

A NEW WORLD

...so what on Earth will they call it?

A BRITISH astronomer has found a new planet in our solar system, The Sun can sensationally reveal.

It is the first discovered since ancient times.

By GAZ GIANT, Sun Spaceman

Last night debate was raging over what to call it.

Contenders range from "Georgium Sidus" — after the King — to, ahem, "Uranus" after an unfortunate-sounding Greek god. The planet has been fleetingly spotted before, but was thought to be a star.

Keen stargazer William Herschel, 42, has now "formally" discovered it with a home-made telescope at his house in Bath.

20 Toilet Jokes — Page 43

ASTRONOMICAL ODDS

2-1: Georgium Sidus (meaning George's Star).

5-1: Herschel (after man who found it).

15-1: Astrea, a goddess mentioned by the Latin poet Ovid.

50-1: Minerva, Roman goddess of crafts and wisdom.

10,000-1: Uranus, father of Saturn in classical mythology.

1785 GEOLOGY: BIRTH OF A NEW SCIENCE

Layers of time Section of the Earth's crust, showing the arrangement of the rock strata (sedimentary rocks) and larger areas of rocks formed by heat (igneous and metamorphic rocks).

JAMES Hutton's revolutionary idea that our landscape was formed over an enormous period was effectively the beginning of geology as a science. It was controversial too – outraging a society which believed that the Bible held proof of the Earth being created no more than 6,000 years earlier.

In the 1650s, an Irish archbishop named James Ussher (1581–1656) attempted to work out the date of 'creation' as described in the Bible. He traced the lineage of Biblical characters, consulted historical documents and arrived at an exact date: 23rd October 4004 BC. This result was widely publicised and many people accepted it without question.

But around that time lived Danish scientist Nicolaus Steno (Danish name Niels Stenson, 1638–1686), one of the first people to take a scientific approach to geology. Steno suggested that layers, or strata, of rocks are laid down one after the other – so the oldest ones are at the bottom. By differentiating between layers, Steno divided Earth's history into different phases, or eras. The division of geological time into eras remains a major feature of modern geology.

Too young Archbishop James Ussher, whose mistaken chronology of the Earth held back progress in geology.

The following century, two opposing schools of thought arose to explain the rock formations. One suggested Earth's rocks were all laid down over a short period, in a worldwide ocean.

The other, pioneered by Hutton (1726–1797), held that the landscape was shaped gradually over a very long time by processes that were still ongoing. In other words, he said, rocks are still being formed – a revolutionary idea at the time.

Hutton suggested that the centre of the Earth is very hot and that some rocks that are solid now were once molten (igneous rocks) – ideas hard for many to accept. He also claimed the heat from Earth's core drives mountain-building and volcanoes.

That was in the 1780s. It was the 1820s before Hutton's ideas were generally accepted.

Since then, geology has matured into a truly modern science. One of the most important new theories was plate tectonics, developed in the 1960s. This suggests that the Earth's crust is made up of fragments called 'plates' which are moving around on an ocean of molten rock (lava). Where

plates collide the crust ruffles up, earthquakes are common and mountains form. At the boundary between plates that are moving apart, lava can leak out, forming brand new rock. The evidence for this theory is overwhelming and the boundaries between the crust's plates are well known.

Dinosaur bone

People had been collecting small fossils for thousands of years. But no one had seen anything like the one that English museum curator Robert Plot (1640–1696) discovered in 1676. Plot suggested that it was the femur (thigh bone) of a giant. It is now known to be from a dinosaur scientists named Megalosaurus.

Until the 17th century, surprisingly few people had suggested that fossils are the remains of plants and animals – it was difficult to see how living things could become encased in solid rock. When it was clear that the Earth was very old, people began to realise the truth about fossils – and that some of the species they held no longer existed. This was crucial in the development of the theory of evolution in the 19th century.

MIND BOGGLER
● Most of the world's coal, which is formed from trillions of plants, appears in rock strata about 300 million years old – from the Carboniferous period.

Fossil teeth Drawing by Nicolaus Steno, who realised that fossils that looked like sharks' teeth really were sharks' teeth, and not 'tongue stones' that had fallen from the sky.

Old rock This *Acasta gneiss* from Northwest Canada is one of the oldest samples of rock ever found – it is 4 billion years old.

WHAT IN THE WORLD?

1782 James Watt (1736–1819) patents the double-acting steam engine.

1782 King George III appoints William Herschel (1738–1822) as King's Astronomer.

1783 The Montgolfier brothers – Joseph (1740–1810) and Jacques (1745–1799) – give their first public demonstration of the hot air balloon they have invented.

1783 French physicist Jacques Charles (1746–1823) invents the hydrogen balloon.

1784 American statesman and inventor Benjamin Franklin (1706–1790) invents bifocal lenses.

NOW JUMP TO... ◐ BIG BANG page 6; ◑ EVOLUTION page 64

THE Sun

onday, April 4, 1785   Three farthings

'PROOF' ON GIANT BONE

THE Hutton report may confirm the outlandish theory over the large mystery bone (left) unearthed in Cornwall in 1676.

Its keeper Robert Plot, from Oxford, thought it was from a giant extinct beast.

And if Earth is millions of years old, as Hutton claims, it could easily have been home to all manner of odd animals now buried under layers of rock.

WORLD EXCLUSIVE

HUTTON REPORT LEAKED

- **Earth millions of years old, says expert on rocks**

- **He rubbishes Old Testament's 6,000yrs claim**

- **Our planet's steaming hot in centre, he insists**

- **He says: I'll reveal the lot.. in 2,138 pages**

By DAWN O'TYME

GEOLOGIST James Hutton turned world history on its head last night — by revealing our planet may be MILLIONS of years old.

The Scot is convinced that layers of rock he has been studying would have taken FAR longer to form than the 6,000 years the Earth is said to have existed for. Hutton, 59, a trained doctor AND lawyer, also claims Earth is molten hot in the middle. He plans to tell all in a 2,138-page book — but The Sun has a leaked copy of his theory, to be read to the Royal Society of Edinburgh today. Hutton (above) says "geological time" boggles the mind. He said: "We find no vestige of a beginning." His claims will enrage almost everyone, since they contradict the Bible's Creation story.

Rock Legend — Pages 4 and 5

● 45

1796 VACCINATION – A MEDICAL MIRACLE

ENGLISH doctor Edward Jenner performed the first vaccination in 1796 – and was met with considerable scepticism from a public worried about its safety and effectiveness. But in the two centuries since, the technique has saved millions of lives and eradicated smallpox – once a feared killer.

Smallpox first appeared more than 3,000 years ago and has been one of humanity's greatest afflictions. It claimed an estimated 300 million lives in the 20th century alone. In Jenner's day, it was responsible for one in ten infant deaths.

People had long noticed that smallpox survivors never caught the disease again – they became immune to it. The same goes for many other infectious diseases. When the body is exposed to a new bacteria or virus, the immune system produces chemicals called antibodies tailor-made to destroy them. Those antibodies become a permanent feature of the immune system, in case of future infection with the same disease.

Vaccines contain bacteria or viruses that have been deactivated or weakened, or in some cases that cause a similar but much less serious disease. They make our bodies produce the necessary antibodies without suffering the devastating impact of the full disease.

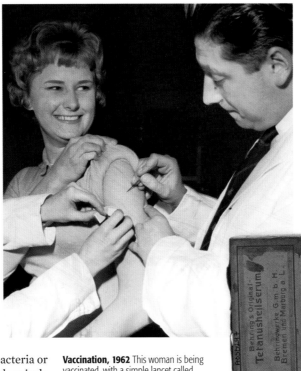

Vaccination, 1962 This woman is being vaccinated, with a simple lancet called a bifurcated needle, as part of a mass programme of vaccination against smallpox.

Tetanus vaccine, c. 1915 German professor Emil von Behring (1854–1917) won the Nobel prize for developing vaccines against diphtheria and tetanus.

MIND BOGGLER
● The word 'vaccination' comes from the Latin for cow, *vacca*.

Before Jenner (1749–1823) attempted vaccination, doctors were using 'variolation' to make people immune to smallpox. Variolation relied on there being two types of smallpox. Pus taken from someone with the weaker form was rubbed into a small incision in the skin of a healthy person. Patients would suffer mild symptoms, including pustules, but most recovered and were then immune to both forms of the disease.

Variolation, also called inoculation, had been used for centuries across Asia. It was introduced to Britain by the English author Mary Montagu (1689–1762), who had seen it in Constantinople. There were risks with the technique: the weaker strain of smallpox was still life threatening and contagious. Patients who had been inoculated had to remain isolated, often for weeks, and about one in a hundred died.

Jenner's breakthrough was to use pus from someone with cowpox, which is not life-threatening. Farmers in his native Gloucestershire noticed that milkmaids who had had cowpox never contracted smallpox – they seemed to be immune. The boy Jenner vaccinated, James Phipps (1788-1853), suffered mild symptoms of cowpox after the treatment. A few weeks later, Jenner inoculated him with smallpox. Phipps suffered none of the normal symptoms of people who were inoculated – he was immune to smallpox.

An act of Parliament in 1840 outlawed variolation and ensured smallpox vaccination would be free for everyone. Thirteen years later another act made it compulsory for every newborn in Britain to be vaccinated.

In 1880, French biologist Louis Pasteur (1822–1895) discovered a second vaccine, against cholera in chickens. A year later he found a vaccine against anthrax and in 1884 a vaccine against rabies in dogs.

Today there are dozens of vaccines and widescale vaccination programmes have controlled or eradicated several deadly diseases.

As for smallpox, the World Health Organisation began a global vaccination and public health initiative in 1967. In that year, two million people died from the disease. Since 1979, there has not been a single case.

WHAT IN THE WORLD?

1788 The first convicts are sent out to Botany Bay, Australia.

1789 George Washington (1732–1799) becomes U.S. president.

1789 The storming of the Bastille heralds the beginning of the French Revolution.

1791 The metric system of measurement is formulated in France.

1791 Italian scientist Luigi Galvani (1737–1798) makes dead frogs' legs twitch by connecting wires of two different metals.

1792 French inventor Claude Chappe (1763–1805) demonstrates the first practical telecommunications system, a system of semaphore towers.

1793 British admiralty begins supplying citrus juice to navy crews to prevent scurvy.

To the point These vaccination lancets were used by Edward Jenner to vaccinate against smallpox.

Vaccine gun 'Med-E Jet' vaccination gun, designed to deliver many doses of smallpox vaccine in rapid succession, as part of the mass vaccination programme. In the event, the simple 'bifurcated needle' was preferred.

NOW JUMP TO... ● PASTEUR page 66; ● SANITATION page 72

THE Sun

Saturday, July 2, 1796   Three farthings

A POX ON YOU, DOCTOR

Jabber the nut ...Jenner attacks James yesterday

Maniac medic gives disease to child in evil 'jab' experiment

By MAL PRACTICE, Medical Correspondent

AN evil doctor caused fury last night — by injecting a boy with SMALLPOX in a twisted experiment.

Crackpot Edward Jenner has already injected James Phipps, eight, with cowpox, which made him ill. He has now given the lad a dose of the deadly disease, hoping the cowpox jab will somehow protect him.

One medical expert stormed: "This man should be struck off, then hanged."

One in three smallpox victims dies. Survivors are often left horribly scarred.

Last night little James seemed OK . . . for now. His parents, asked by The Sun why they allowed him to be abused by Jenner, would not comment.

Jenner, 47, of Berkeley, Gloucs, made his name studying the nesting habits of the **CUCKOO.**

The Sun's doctor Arfur Brain said: "People like him give my profession a bad name. The application of leeches is a proven cure for disease. Why he would try anything else is beyond me."

Nail Doctor Death — Pages 4 & 5

Tried and trusted... the leech

● 47

1800 VOLTA'S BATTERY: ELECTRICITY ON TAP

THE FIRST battery was made by Italian scientist Alessandro Volta. His simple invention evolved into an invaluable piece of technology for the modern world. It also played a vital role in advancing scientific understanding of matter and energy in the 19th century.

Again and again An early lead-acid accumulator, from about 1860. Invented by Gaston Planté, these were the first rechargeable batteries.

Animal electricity Italian physicist Luigi Galvani, whose discovery of 'animal electricity' led to the invention of the battery.

Volta was inspired by the intriguing discovery of another Italian scientist, Luigi Galvani (1737–1798).

In the 1780s, Galvani was experimenting with 'animal electricity', making the muscles of animals' dismembered limbs move during electrical storms and when stimulated by electrostatic generators. Galvani found that frogs' legs twitched whenever they were touched by two different metals at once – even with no outside source of electricity. Galvani wrongly believed the power was coming from the nerves in the frogs' legs.

Volta (1745–1827) realised the electricity was generated by the interaction between the metals, not by the frogs' legs, and made his battery to prove it. The device was a pile of copper and zinc discs, interspersed with cardboard ones. The cardboard discs were soaked in salt water to increase conductivity.

In 1802, English surgeon-chemist William Cruickshank improved the design. In the 'Voltaic Pile', the weight of the metal discs squeezed out the salt water from the cardboard discs, so the battery never lasted very long and was limited in height and therefore power. Cruickshank's battery was horizontal, with copper and zinc plates arranged in a trough. The salt water, or sometimes dilute acid, sat in the trough so the battery did not dry out.

Having a handy source of power – rather than 'static' electricity that could not easily be controlled – greatly increased the pace of scientific discovery.

The battery allowed physicists to investigate the nature of electricity itself. The relationship between voltage, current and electrical resistance – known as Ohm's Law – was

MIND BOGGLER

● Luigi Galvani's experiments with frogs' legs were an inspiration for Mary Shelley's book *Frankenstein*.

discovered in 1827 by German physicist Georg Ohm (1759–1854).

The battery led to the discovery of electromagnetism in 1820 by Danish physicist Hans Christian Ørsted (1777–1851). And it helped to found a new science, electrochemistry.

Scientists realised they would be able to use batteries to separate compounds, producing pure samples of elements. By 1809 English scientist Humphry Davy (1778–1829) had managed to extract several metals never before prepared pure, including sodium, potassium and magnesium.

More powerful and reliable batteries were made with new combinations of metals and electrolytes. More portable, dry batteries followed. French physicist Gaston Planté (1834–1889) invented the first rechargeable battery in 1859. It was a 'lead-acid' accumulator – very similar to the batteries used to start car engines today.

Chemical reaction Reconstruction of an early experiment by Humphry Davy, passing electric current from a Cruickshank trough battery through solid potash (potassium carbonate).

NOW JUMP TO... ◐ ELECTRICITY & MAGNETISM page 38; ◑ ELECTRIC MACHINES page 50

WHAT IN THE WORLD?

1797 The Bank of England issues the first ever pound note.

1798 English clergyman Thomas Malthus (1766–1834) predicts that overpopulation will lead to war, famine and disease.

1799 The Rosetta Stone is discovered, by French soldiers, in Egypt – it provides clues which eventually enable people to read Egyptian hieroglyphics.

1799 American inventor Eli Whitney (1765–1825) develops the 'American System of Manufacturing', the first mass production.

1799 A perfectly preserved mammoth is found buried in permafrost in Siberia.

Nowadays batteries are used in a huge variety of machines and everyday gadgets such as watches, remote controls and the iPod.

Splitting water

Six weeks after Volta announced his battery to the world in 1800, English scientists William Nicholson (1753–1815) and Anthony Carlisle (1768–1842) made their own. While they were testing it, they added some water to one end to make a better contact. Immediately, bubbles of gas came from the water.

The two scientists reasoned that the gases were hydrogen and oxygen, already known to be the constituent elements of water. They inserted one wire from each end of their pile into a small tube containing water, and confirmed that hydrogen gas appeared at one wire, oxygen at the other.

Dry cell Experimental Leclanché cell, the forerunner of the 'dry cell', which was once the most popular type of battery. Today, it has been replaced by the alkaline battery, which is nevertheless based upon a similar reaction.

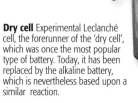

THE Sun

One penny

day, March 21, 1800

r guy . . . Nicholson

lee as it zaps ater to oduce xygen

**y ANNE ODE
d KATH ODE**

English experi- er claims he has water into two s using his OWN -style gizmo.

liam Nicholson, nd from London, aid to have got of Volta's inven- and built his own. then attached to it and trailed in water.

en electric cur- flowed, oxygen les formed on the of one wire, and ogen bubbles on other.

t night there was t excitement over process, which he "electrolysis".

ientists believe applying electric- rom a battery to sorts of chemicals split them apart, ing pure samples arious elements to nade.

Billy's ubbly ubbly!

EE PAGE 9

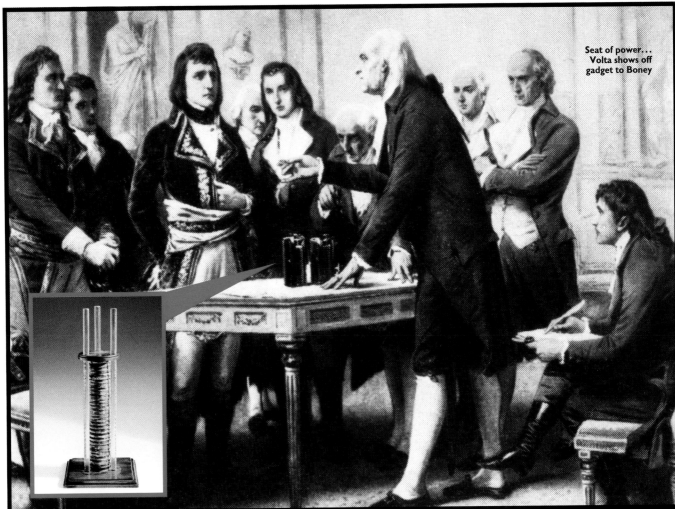

Seat of power... Volta shows off gadget to Boney

POWER ARRANGER

Volta's 'battery' makes stream of electricity

EXCLUSIVE by EVA REDDIE

SPARKY scientist Alessandro Volta has invented an amazing device that produces a stream of electricity.

The 55-year-old Italian's complex "Voltaic Pile" *(inset)* is made of metal discs and soggy cardboard.

France's ruler Napoleon was stunned when Volta showed it to him. A scientist said last night: "It's the least we can do now to name a unit of electricity after him."

Batteries, Will They Last? See Page 8

1821 THE ORIGINS OF ELECTRIC MACHINES

THE VAST array of electrical devices we take for granted today can be traced back to the discoveries of British scientist Michael Faraday who, during his long career, made the first motor, generator and transformer.

Faraday's electric motor of 1821 depended on a discovery a year earlier by Danish scientist Hans Christian Ørsted. While preparing for a lecture about electricity, Ørsted noticed how an electric current in a wire made a nearby magnetic compass needle twitch. The current was making magnetism, a phenomenon called 'electromagnetism'.

British scientist Humphry Davy, Faraday's mentor, realised an electromagnetic force should be able to produce sustained motion, not just a twitch. But he couldn't make a device to achieve it. Faraday did – by suspending a wire in a pool of mercury with a magnet in it. Current made the wire whirl around the magnet.

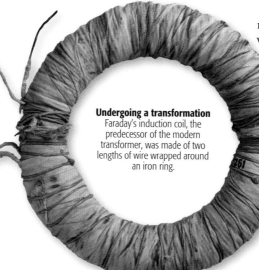

Undergoing a transformation Faraday's induction coil, the predecessor of the modern transformer, was made of two lengths of wire wrapped around an iron ring.

When Faraday wrote about his motor, he forgot to mention Davy's involvement. Davy was furious and as a result Faraday temporarily stopped work on electromagnetism.

Other scientists carried on the research. In 1825, English physicist William Sturgeon realised he could strengthen the electromagnetic force by wrapping the current-carrying wire into a coil around an iron bar. He had made the first electromagnet.

Humphry Davy died in 1829, and Faraday (1791–1867) resumed his work on electromagnetism. He discovered that moving a magnet to and fro made current flow in a wire nearby. He found the same thing happened if the wire moved instead of the magnet. This is called electromagnetic induction – the magnet 'induces' electric forces in the wire. This forms the basis of electric generators, and Faraday made a simple generator in 1831.

The same year he made what was effectively the first transformer. The modern world depends heavily on these to increase or decrease the voltage of a supply. Electricity is normally produced in power stations at 30,000 volts, but is 'transformed' to much higher voltages for efficient transmission along power lines. Then it is transformed down again in a series of steps before reaching our homes at 230 volts. Many devices inside our homes such as mobile phone chargers contain small transformers that change the voltage of mains electricity, typically down to 6, 9 or 12 volts.

Faraday also introduced the idea of electric and magnetic 'fields'. He was the first to draw their shapes and show how they interact.

Faraday was a great experimental scientist and innovator who also made important discoveries in chemistry and became well-known for popularising science through his public lectures at the Royal Institution in London.

One of his friends, the brilliant Scottish physicist James Clerk Maxwell, developed Faraday's ideas about electric and magnetic fields into a mathematical theory. In the 1860s, he derived four equations to describe their behaviour.

By combining those four equations into one, Maxwell discovered that electromagnetic fields oscillate, and radiate through space in waves. According to his equation, the wave's speed is identical to the speed of light. He had proved light is an electromagnetic wave.

Radio waves, microwaves, infrared, ultraviolet, X-rays and gamma rays are also electromagnetic radiation, although not all were known in Maxwell's day.

Moving out James Clerk Maxwell, whose inspired mathematical equations united electricity, magnetism and light.

Generating interest A permanent magnet being moved into and out of a coil of wire. The meter on the bench measures the electric current produced.

WHAT IN THE WORLD?

1801 Britain's first census; the population was 8,872,000.
1803 English engineer Richard Trevithick builds the first steam locomotive.
1805 Admiral Horatio Nelson defeats the French navy in the battle of Trafalgar, and dies during the battle.
1807 The slave trade is abolished in Britain.
1808 English scientist John Dalton publishes convincing proof of the existence of atoms.
1809 Canning is perfected as a method of preserving food, by French inventor Nicolas Appert.
1813 English inventor William Hedley patents the first practical steam locomotive, 'Puffing Billy'.
1815 Humphry Davy invents the miners' safety lamp.
1818 Mary Shelley publishes her novel *Frankenstein*.

MIND BOGGLER
● The world's smallest electric motor is less than one-hundredth the width of a human hair. It is made of tiny molten metal droplets inside a carbon 'nanotube'.

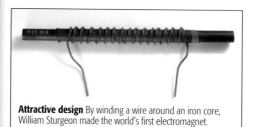

Attractive design By winding a wire around an iron core, William Sturgeon made the world's first electromagnet.

NOW JUMP TO... ● **ELECTRICITY & MAGNETISM page 38; ● THE LIGHT BULB page 70**

NICE MOTOR

Whirling wire gadget could form machines of the future

Creating a buzz . . . current sends wire spinning round magnet in pool of mercury

EXCLUSIVE by MAGGIE NETICKS

THIS incredible little gadget is the first proof that electricity can be used to power machines.

The "motor", invented by scientist Michael Faraday, 30, is a piece of wire hanging into a pool of mercury which has a magnet in it.

When current from a battery is sent down the wire, it whizzes round and round the magnet — proving that the electricity is creating a magnetic field. And if the whole procedure is reversed, it actually **CREATES** power.

Although the device is basic, experts predict it could lead to enormous advances in technology if used on a bigger scale.

Faraday's discovery is a kick in the teeth for his ex-boss, top chemist and physicist Sir Humphry Davy, whose own attempts to build an electric motor failed.

Faraday *(right)* is a humble, self-taught blacksmith's son from South London who was so poor as a child he had to make a loaf of bread last him a week.

He learned about chemistry as Davy's down-trodden assistant.

One scientific source said last night: "What Faraday has discovered could change the world.

"Humphry Davy is a great scientist — but when people look back at his life they'll probably say his best discovery was Faraday!"

Animal Magnetism — Page 9

1822 CHARLES BABBAGE, COMPUTER PIONEER

CHARLES Babbage designed an automatic computer more than 100 years before the first electronic ones. None of his inventions was completed in his lifetime, but engineers at the Science Museum finally built one to Babbage's design in 1991. It showed just how far ahead of his time he was.

The predecessors of mechanical calculators were built long before Babbage. 'Napier's Bones', invented in 1617 by Scottish mathematician John Napier (1550–1617), consisted of multiplication tables etched into wooden rods. By lining up the rods and adding up numbers across adjacent rods, large numbers could be multiplied easily.

The first mechanical device to add, subtract and – by incorporating Napier's Bones, multiply – was made by German astronomer Wilhelm Schickard (1592–1635) in 1623. Nearly 20 years later, French mathematician Blaise Pascal (1623–1662) produced a calculator, but it could only add and subtract. In 1671, German mathematician and philosopher Gottfried von Leibniz (1646–1716) improved on Pascal's design, producing a machine to add, subtract, multiply and divide.

Faced with very complex calculations, scientists and engineers in the 19th century relied on numerical tables – reference books filled with numbers. These were laboriously prepared by people called 'calculators' who did the sums by hand. Babbage (1791–1871), an English mathematician, wanted to replace them with machines, backing his argument up with the amount of errors that crept into their work. In 1821, he decided to design a machine to carry out the arithmetic – and received substantial Government funding to do so.

Napier's Bones A set of rotating Napier's Bones, from the second half of the 17th century. Each rod carries the multiplication tables of the numbers from 0 to 9.

Making a difference Babbage's Difference Engine Number 2 was finally realised in 1991, by engineers at the Science Museum. This is the 'addition carriage mechanism'. The 2.6-tonne machine has 4,000 separate parts

Count on it This calculator, made by Blaise Pascal, could carry out simple arithmetic thanks to carefully-designed cogs inside.

MIND BOGGLER
● The world's first electronic desktop calculator was made by the Bell Punch Company of England, and first went on sale in 1961. It weighed 16 pounds (7.3 kg), and cost £355 (equivalent to about £5,000 today)

Babbage's mechanical computer would use a mathematical technique called the method of differences. This allowed complex equations, which machines could NOT do, to be worked out using only addition and subtraction, which they COULD do. Even today's electronic computers can only add, subtract and compare numbers: all of their complex mathematical operations are based on these simple ones, done extremely rapidly.

Babbage's ambitious Difference Engine, designed around 1822, was on a different scale from any early calculating machines. It would store and manipulate several 20-digit numbers and output the results automatically. During the 1820s, Babbage worked on new manufacturing techniques necessary for its construction, but in the end only fragments were ever built and tested.

In 1837 Babbage designed another computer which would carry out multi-stage calculations and be fully programmable. Powered by a steam engine, with a program input on punched cards and a working 'memory', Babbage's Analytical Engine would have been the first all-purpose computer. I was never built.

Babbage returned to the idea of his Difference Engine. During the 1840s, he improved his original design and called the result Difference Engine Number 2. It was this design that a Science Museum team built in 1991 using technology available during the 19th century. It has 4,000 moving parts, weighs 2.6 tonnes, is 2.1 metres (7ft) high and 3.3 metres (11ft) long. Impressively, when the machine was complete, and the handles cranked, it produced the correct answers to a set of complex equations. The results were 31 digits long. In 2000, the museum also built a working printer that Babbage designed to output his results.

William Herschel
German-born William Herschel (1738-1822) was the first person to discover a planet with a telescope – Uranus – and became the 'King's astronomer'. He was knighted in 1816. You can read more about his life on page 42.

Babbage's printer In 2000, engineers at the Science Museum completed Babbage's printer, designed for use with his Difference Engine and his Analytical Engine.

WHAT IN THE WORLD?
1821 German astronomer Friedrich Wilhelm Bessel (1784–1846) begins a catalogue of 50,000 stars – it will take him 12 years to complete.

1821 Greece declares independence from the Ottoman Empire.

1821 The USA takes over Florida, which it bought from Spain.

1821 George IV is crowned King of Britain and Ireland.

NOW JUMP TO... ● EARLY CALCULATOR page 30; ● COMPUTING page 110

STARGAZER WILL'S DEAD

Stellar career . . . Herschel

TOP astronomer Sir William Herschel — the man who discovered Uranus — died last night aged 83. The "King's Astronomer", from Slough, was also famous for discovering infrared radiation and for a series of stunning breakthroughs on the solar system and Milky Way. A space expert said: "When it comes to astronomy, he was a star."

Boffin got hundreds of pounds of our cash to build computer... O WHERE IS IT?

bbage . . .
en fortune
handouts

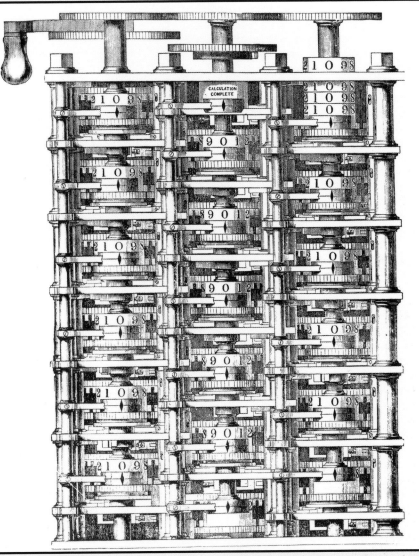

Con-puter . . . Babbage's 'difference' engine, cranked by handle, is still on the drawing board

WE'VE BEEN ADD!

A MATHS genius given a small fortune in taxpayers' money to build a mechanical "computer" has STILL not made it.

And last night The Sun led a chorus of

By IVAN IDEA

protests over how our money is being spent.

Cambridge-educated Charles Babbage convinced the Government to fund the proposed computer.

He said it would eliminate human error in large

calculations. He drew up a fancy plan for the "difference engine" — about 8ft high and comprising a staggering 25,000 parts.

But there is **NO** sign of it being made. Yet Babbage has asked for **MORE** money — despite working on **ANOTHER** machine.
Sum You Lose — Page 11

1826 THE PIONEERS OF PHOTOGRAPHY

THE FIRST photograph was made by French inventor Joseph Nicéphore Niépce after years of experimenting to produce a permanent image from a camera. Within a century, millions of people owned cameras.

The ancestor of the modern camera is the camera obscura, the earliest of which were small, dark rooms with a small hole to let in light. The image of the scene outside the room would form on its back wall, upside down. From the 16th century, artists used camera obscuras to help produce lifelike images that they would trace around. Portable versions were eventually made.

Niépce (1765–1833) wanted somehow to 'fix' the image the camera obscura produced and began trying out various chemicals to achieve it. He succeeded with a petrochemical called 'bitumen of Judea', spread on to a pewter plate.

His earliest surviving photograph, on the page opposite, needed an estimated eight-hour exposure to bright sunlight to produce. Niépce called the process 'heliography', meaning 'sun writing'.

From 1829, he worked with another Frenchman, Louis Daguerre (1787–1851), to try to improve the technique. The two experimented with other substances, including silver.

Niépce died in 1833 and Daguerre continued the research. By 1838, he had perfected the 'daguerreotype', an image formed on

Light boxes Camera, mid-1830s, belonging to Talbot. Early cameras were simple wooden boxes with a lens and an opening to insert a photographic plate or, in this case, photographic paper.

Gentlemen's club Print from a Calotype negative 1843. The Calotype process was invented by Talbot, who appears in the photograph. The men posing for the picture would have had to stand very still for a few seconds.

a silver-plated copper sheet. Before a picture was taken, the silver surface was 'sensitised', by exposure to iodine vapour. This formed a light-sensitive compound called silver iodide. After the picture was taken, the image was developed and then fixed using various chemicals. This was the first commercially available photographic technology.

Britain's pioneer of photography was William Henry Fox Talbot (1800–1877), who carried out his first experiments at the same time as Daguerre. Like Daguerre's process, Talbot's 'calotype' system exploited the fact that compounds of silver produce tiny granules of pure silver when exposed to light. Talbot's images were produced as 'negatives' on paper, and multiple 'positive' copies could be printed from each one.

Both these methods were clumsy and complicated. New developments focussed on more convenient ways to attach the silver compounds to photographic plates, and on reducing exposure times. The most successful was invented in the 1870s by Richard Maddox (1816–1902) and used gelatin to bind the silver compound to the plate. Gelatin is still used in most camera film today.

Until the late 1880s, photography was largely in the hands of professionals who would buy or prepare their own photographic plates and develop the images themselves. In 1884, American inventor George Eastman (1854–1932) pioneered the use of film on rolls, first with paper and from 1889 with celluloid. Eastman started the Kodak company, which brought photography to ordinary people with its Brownie camera (1900).

The first commercially successful technology for taking colour photographs was the autochrome process – colour photographs made on glass. The first colour film, celluloid with layers of emulsion sensitive to different colours, was available in the 1930s.

Today, digital photography has become hugely popular. The cameras are much the same, but the image is captured as electrical signals instead of a collection of silver granules.

Roll on George Eastman, whose company, Kodak, pioneered the use of roll film, making photography cheaper, simpler and accessible to more people.

In the picture Photography pioneer Joseph Niepce.

Silver face Daguerreotype photograph, from the 1840s, of Louis Daguerre.

MIND BOGGLER

- In July 2006 six photographers converted an aircraft hangar in California into the world's largest pinhole camera, and took the world's largest photo – 8.5 by 32 metres (28 by 108 feet).

WHAT IN THE WORLD?

1823 English physicist William Sturgeon (1783–1850) makes the first true electromagnet.

1824 German astronomer Joseph von Fraunhofer (1787–1826) invents a clockwork device that moves large telescopes automatically, counteracting the Earth's spin.

1824 English builder Joseph Aspadin patents Portland cement.

1824 Edinburgh city council founds the first fire brigade in Britain.

1825 English scientist Michael Faraday (1791–1867) isolates benzene from whale oil.

1825 Menai Straits Bridge, Wales, covers a width of 176 metres (579 ft) in a single span, heralding the beginning of modern bridge-building.

1825 Hans Christian Ørsted (1777–1851) isolates the element aluninium.

NOW JUMP TO... ⊘ CINEMA page 76; ⊘ TELEVISION page 94

THE Sun

PAGE 3

WATCH THIS SPACE
'Picture' brainwave to brighten up our Page 3

Wednesday, June 14, 1826   One penny

PICTURE EXCLUSIVE

FIRST PICTURE OF FIRST PICTURE

Miracle of image made by camera

By LEN SCAPPON

THIS is the incredible first image produced by a miracle process dubbed "heliography".

Inventor Joseph Niépce, 61, got it by pointing his camera at a building for eight hours.

The picture appeared on a metal plate he covered in chemicals. Niépce, from France, hopes to capture more interesting images soon.

INSIDE: MORE SENSATIONAL DEVELOPMENTS

1829 STEAM ENGINES AND RAILWAYS

BRITAIN was the first country to have an Industrial Revolution, between about 1760 and 1840. It was made possible by the production of iron, and by people's ingenuity, but it was driven by steam. In the late 18th century, steam engines turned the wheels of industry. And in the 19th century, steam was responsible for another revolution: railways.

Mining was important in the lead-up to the Industrial Revolution – for obtaining coal and metal ores. So the frequent and unavoidable flooding of mines was a major inconvenience. In 1698 Englishman Thomas Savery (1650–1715) made a pump that could reliably raise water about ten metres (30 feet) by 'suction', created as steam condensed. This was not enough for use in mines but Savery's machine was used to pump water supplies in London.

Cornish inventor Thomas Newcomen (1663–1729) was the first to make a practical steam-driven pumping engine, in 1712. Newcomen engines quickly became part of the industrial landscape of coal mining areas. His machine also used the 'suction' created by condensing steam. It was an 'atmospheric' steam engine, which means the work involved in pumping was done by the pressure of the atmosphere pushing down on a piston. The steam was important because it filled a cylinder underneath the piston; cold water injected into the cylinder made the steam condense, so that it took up almost no space, leaving the pressure of the air outside the cylinder to push the piston down. The piston was connected to a pump.

The next major advance was down to Scottish instrument maker James Watt (1736–1819). In 1765 he improved Newcomen's engine by having the steam condense in a separate tank connected to the main cylinder by a pipe. This meant the engine's cylinder could be kept hot all the time, improving efficiency. In 1788, Watt came up with a way of changing the up-and-down motion

Pump it up Thomas Savery's steam 'suction pump', patented in 1698, designed to lift water from flooded mines. It was not very successful.

Beam engine Thomas Newcomen's pumping engine. The boiler heated water to produce steam, which filled the cylinder above. Cold water injected into the cylinder makes the steam condense, and atmospheric pressure pushes the piston down, lifting the other end of the beam, which is connected to a pump.

Under pressure Richard Trevithick, the engineer who designed a steam engine that could withstand high pressures. His engine led directly to the development of railway locomotives.

of the piston into a circular one. Suddenly, steam engines could do much more than just pump. Watt's rotary steam engines began to replace water and wind power in mills and factories.

In 1797 another Cornish inventor, Richard Trevithick (1771–1833), produced a more compact steam engine just as powerful as Watt's. It used heated, high-pressure steam – something Watt considered too dangerous. Trevithick's engines were powerful enough to drive road wheels and carry themselves along, and in 1803 he made the world's first steam locomotive. The other ingredient of the railways – the rails – already carried horse-drawn wagons in and out of mines.

Engineer George Stephenson (1781–1848) had heard of a railway being built from Stockton to access a rich seam of coal at Darlington. He suggested a steam locomotive would pull more wagons than horses could and built a locomotive for the line. The 13-kilometre (8-mile)

NOW JUMP TO... ➔ **THE MOTOR CAR** page 74; ➔ **POWERED FLIGHT** page 84

WHAT IN THE WORLD?

1827 French physicist André Ampère (1775–1836) works out an equation expressing the magnetic force between two wires carrying electric current.

1828 Astronomers are convinced that deflections in Uranus' orbit are caused by the influence of another planet. That planet, Neptune, is discovered in 1846.

Stockton-to-Darlington railway, which opened in 1825, took passengers too but only in carriages hauled by cable. Only the coal trucks were pulled by the locomotive.

Soon afterwards work began on the Liverpool to Manchester Railway. When it was nearing completion, five locomotives took part in the 'Rainhill Trials', a competition to find the best one to pull the carriages. One was Rocket, chiefly designed and built by Robert Stephenson (1803–1859), overseen by his father George. Rocket won and was the basis of the locomotives used when the line opened. It was the first in the world where passengers were pulled along by a steam locomotive.

Railways quickly spread throughout Britain and the world and became the main mode of land transport for nearly a century until eclipsed by the car.

Nowadays Britain has more than 10,000 miles of track – and more than two billion rail journeys are made each year.

Early typewriter

American inventor William Austin Burt (1792–1858) invented one of the first writing machines – the typographer – in 1829. It was a predecessor to the typewriter, the first practical examples of which appeared in the 1870s.

MIND BOGGLER
● Japanese high speed 'bullet' trains travel at an average speed of more than 260 km/h (160 mph).

Round and round James Watt's rotative engine of 1788. This engine worked like Newcomen's (above, centre), but the cogwheel, called a 'sun-and-planet' gear, changed the up-and-down into round-and-round motion. This engine's separate condenser also made it more efficient than Newcomen's.

STEPHENSON'S ROCKET

THE Sun

Thursday, October 15, 1829   One penny

BOX 'WRITES' (SLOWLY)

MACHINE that "writes" using lead type has been launched. The "typographer" (far right) is a wooden box with type mounted on a metal wheel. The user turns a crank to line up the right letter, then pulls a lever which stamps the inked letter into the paper. The snag is that even its U.S. inventor William Burt writes faster by hand. *Not My Type — Page 21*

CHUFFED TO BITS

Stephenson's Rocket wins loco prize

Champ . . . Rocket took Rainhill glory

By IVOR ENGINE

ENGINEER George Stephenson was dead chuff-chuffed last night as "Rocket" dramatically won the Rainhill Trials.

It means Rocket will be the blueprint for steam locos on the world's first passenger railway, from Liverpool to Manchester.

A crowd of 10,000 watched the little engine beat four rivals, completing the 35-mile course at more than 10mph. All the others broke down.

Ticket To Chaos — Pages 4 & 5

Triumph . . . George last night

ONE-WAY TICKET TO DISASTER

Campaigners' rail gloom as Rocket wins loco showdown

By THOMAS TANK

RAILWAYS will b disaster for Bri furious campaig claimed last night.

They gloomily pred they will be **UNS CROWDED, EXPENSIVE** will **POLLUTE** the coun

The attack came as world's first passenger ra took a step nearer comp with "Rocket" winning Rainhill Trials in front ecstatic crowd of about 1

The route, from Liverpo Manchester, could now b and running next year.

But safety groups are fu that people will be roc along at white-knuckle s of more than 10mph.

Environment groups warning of black smoke the locomotives' coal bu being pumped into the ai

And consumer groups woefully pessimistic ove new transport system. predicted that if it takes

●Passengers will pay e tant fares and face cro carriages, often havin stand for long distances.

●Trains will never ru time. Sometimes they wi cancelled for no apparent son and without notice.

●Stations will be cold, lit, smelly and dangerous.

●Staff will be poorly and uniformly unhelpful.

Consumer watchdog Upp said: "It may seem the greatest breakthroug transport since man tame horse, but you wait and s

Lucrative

After yesterday's resu Rainhill, near Liverpoo now know steam engines be built along the lin Rocket, which won the si "trial" hands down.

It was up against four each having to chug 35 – the distance from Live to Manchester – at an av speed of at least 10mph.

All the other four – n Sans Pareil, Novelty, Pers ance and Cycloped – down before finishing.

Rocket, built by father son team George and R Stephenson, went the dis at an average of 12mph, ing 13 tons.

The Stephensons, from castle, pocketed the glit £500 prize – and the luc contract to make locos fo new rail route.

Many spectators were f that Novelty did not win.

One wrote to the local that although Rocket wo prize fair and square, grand prize of public op is one which has been g by Novelty. It is the prin and arrangement London engine which w followed in the constructi all future locomotives.

"The beautiful mechanis the connecting movemen the wheels, the abs absence of all smell, s noise, vibration, or unple feeling of any kind, the gance of the machinery proclaim its perfection."

What a choke . . . our cartoonist paints a dismal picture of how polluted Hyde Park could look once everyone has their own train

SANS PAREIL
DESPITE slightly old-fashioned technology, Sans Pareil was an early contender. It completed eight trips before a pump broke. All is not lost for its makers, though. It has been bought by the railway.

PERSEVERANCE
A DISASTER. Perseverance was damaged on the way to the trials and only took part after five days of repairs. It then limped along at just 6mph and was withdrawn, winning a £25 consolation prize.

CYCLOPED
CYCLOPED was a shambles, powered by a horse walking along the drive belt, like a hamster on a wheel. It was withdrawn from the trials when the poor creature fell through its floor.

NOVELTY
SO nearly the winner, Novelty was lighter and faster than its rivals, hitting a blood-curdling 28mph, but was plagued by a cracked boiler pipe and dropped out last, leaving only Rocket.

ROCKET
THE last engine standing, and therefore the winner. Rocket hauled its load 40 times over a distance of 1¾ miles and for a brief stretch hit 30mph. The Stephensons' reliable design is now set to become the blueprint for all steam locomotives of the future.

1858 BRUNEL – LEGEND OF ENGINEERING

ISAMBARD Kingdom Brunel was a prolific and visionary engineer. The buildings, bridges, tunnels and steamships he left behind are a testament to his ingenuity and to the spirit of sheer determination felt by all the great engineers of the 19th century.

By the end of the Industrial Revolution, the proportion of the British population living in cities had increased from 20 to 80 per cent. The rate of large-scale building projects increased dramatically. The engineers of the 19th century believed they could achieve anything, however ambitious. Their confidence was often challenged, as many projects suffered disasters, unforeseen technical hurdles or financial troubles.

One such project was the Thames Tunnel – under the riverbed between Rotherhithe and Wapping in London – which Brunel began working on in 1823. The chief engineer was his father, French-born Marc Brunel (1769–1849). Many workers died due to the frequent collapses and flooding and the project was halted for long periods. However, it did open in 1843, the first ever tunnel beneath a riverbed.

The Great Exhibition In the 19th century, Britain was the world's leading economic power. The Great Exhibition of 1851, held in the 'Crystal Palace' in South London, symbolised Britain's supremacy. It showed off Britain's manufacturing prowess, and attracted visitors from across Europe.

In 1831, Brunel (1806–1859) became chief engineer at Bristol Docks. Over the next two years he designed several other docks, but in 1833 he moved to the project for which he is best remembered: the Great Western Railway. Britain's railways were still very new and the Bristol to London line would be a vital link. Brunel was chief engineer, designing the innovative bridges, viaducts, terminals and tunnels that characterised the line and made it one of the wonders of 19th century Britain.

Brunel also excelled in marine engineering, important in a country strengthening its trade links with far-flung parts. In the 1830s, a return voyage to New York took two months by sailing ship. Brunel was determined to cut that, so he designed the Great Western, the world's largest steamship at that time. This wooden-hulled paddle steamer, launched in 1837, cut the round trip to 29 days. Spurred on by its success, Brunel designed another steamship, the SS Great Britain. Launched in 1843, it was the first steamship with a metal hull and a 'screw' propeller. But the biggest and most ambitious of Brunel's ships was the Great Eastern, designed to carry passengers non-stop to India and Australia. It had sails, huge paddle wheels and a propeller. Work began in 1852 but like so many other such projects soon ran over budget and was hampered by seemingly insurmountable technical challenges.

The Great Eastern was finally finished in 1858 and made its maiden voyage to New York in 1860, a year after Brunel's death. It was not

MIND BOGGLER
● The world's biggest passenger liner is the Queen Mary 2. Launched in 2004, it is more than twice as long, and five times as heavy, as the Great Eastern.

Under water The Thames Tunnel was the first project Brunel worked on. 50,000 people walked through it on the day it opened. The tunnel is still in use today, as part of London's Underground system.

SS Great Britain Brunel's second ship, the SS Great Britain, shown here shortly after its launch. This was the first steel-hulled, propeller driven steam ship to cross the Atlantic.

No mistake

Hymen Lipman's invention of a rubber attached to a pencil was a good one and still much used today. However, the patent he was awarded in 1858 was withdrawn in 1872 after a court decided he simply combined two existing inventions instead of inventing something original.

the commercial success he an his backers had hoped for, but i did later find an important us laying the first successful transa lantic telegraph cables in 1866.

Five years on from his deat another of Brunel's masterpiece was completed, Bristol's Clifto Suspension Bridge – a further spectacula monument to a great man.

Clifton Suspension Bridge Brunel won a competition aimed at finding a design for a bridge to span the Avon Gorge in Bristol. He did not live to see the bridge, which was finally completed in 1864

WHAT IN THE WORLD?
1845 Irish potato crop fails, causing famine there.
1846 German astronomer Johann Galle (1812–1910) observes planet Neptune after calculations by John Couch Adams and Urbain le Verrier predicted its location.
1848 German revolutionary Karl Marx (1818–1883) publishes Manifest der Kommunistischen Partei (The Communist Manifesto).
1850 The first department store, the Bon Marché, opens in Paris.
1851 The Great Exhibition opens in South London.
1851 French physicist Hippolyte Fizeau (1819–1896) discovers that the speed of light in water is less than in air.
1851 William Thomson (Lord Kelvin, 1824–1907) proposes the absolute temperature scale.
1852 American inventor Elisha Otis (1811–1861) installs the first lift, in a building in New York.
1854 An electric telegraph links London and Paris.
1855 French physiologist Claude Bernard (1813–1878) suggests how a human body maintains a constant environment, a principle known as homeostasis.
1856 English inventor Henry Bessemer (1813–1898) develops the Bessemer process for producing steel.

NOW JUMP TO... ◐ **STEPHENSON'S ROCKET page 56;** ◑ **SANITATION page 72**

THE Sun

...day, January 29, 1858   Penny farthing

New error dawns

A GIANT leap in pencil evolution was announced last night . . . the attachment of a RUBBER.

Inventor Hymen Lipman, of Philadelphia, U.S. has patented the new device — which will allow kids to erase schoolwork errors instantly simply by flipping the pencil upside down and rubbing. A spokesman said: "It's the biggest thing to hit the pencil since its invention in 1564."

Top draw...pencil

Sharpen Up Your Act — Page 2

Hull of an achievement . . . artist's impression of workers at Millwall this week as final preparations were made

MOTHER SHIP

By COLE POWER, Industrial Editor

THE biggest ship in history is ready to launch, The Sun can reveal.

The SS Great Eastern, designed by engineering legend Isambard Kingdom Brunel, can sail 4,000 passengers round the world without refuelling.

Built in Millwall, East London, she weighs 32,000 tons, is 692ft long and 83ft wide. Brunel, 51, has dubbed her the "Great Babe."   **Full Story: Pages 6 & 7**

Brunel: Biggest boat in history set for launch

She's my baby . . . top engineer Brunel in front of ship's colossal chains yesterday

1859 DARWIN'S THEORY OF EVOLUTION

THE THEORY of evolution by English naturalist Charles Darwin was the first truly scientific explanation of the diversity of plants and animals. Its implication that mankind evolved from animals caused a furore. But today it is almost universally accepted by scientists.

In Darwin's day nearly everyone in Europe believed the Old Testament story that God created all living things shortly after making the Earth. Another strong belief was that God created humans fundamentally different from, and superior to, all other animals.

It is easy to see why everyone assumed each species was created a long time ago and had not changed since. Every generation appears identical to the previous one. Each species is well adapted to its surroundings. Complex organic structures – including eyes, hands, flowers and leaves – could easily be the work of a purposeful, intelligent designer. Darwin's theory challenged all these beliefs.

The central idea of evolution is that every organism is related to every other, an idea called 'common descent'. If evolution is correct, you can trace back the lineage of any two species to a common ancestor. The more closely related the species, the more recent their common ancestor.

As a young man Darwin (1809–1882) joined the survey ship HMS Beagle on a scientific expedition around the world. He studied geological formations and wildlife in many countries and noted that certain species seemed related to those elsewhere, while still being slightly different. Many bore remarkable similarities to the fossils of extinct creatures.

Darwin realised that small variations – nowadays we call them 'mutations' – arise randomly and naturally in species. He also saw that plants and animals always produce more offspring than can actually survive. Any mutation that gives an individual animal or plant an advantage in the battle for survival will give it more chance of flourishing and producing offspring. That variation is then likely to be passed on to the next generation, making it the lucky beneficiary of 'natural selection'. Over vast periods of time, a series of tiny, random changes result in major changes to the species. Eventually it has 'evolved' to such an extent that it is a completely new species.

Darwin published his theory in his book *The Origin of the Species by Means of Natural Selection* in 1859. It sparked a public controversy. There were essays and speeches, newspaper cartoons depicting Darwin as a monkey and public protest meetings. People loathed the idea that humans shared common ancestors with all other creatures. Actually, Darwin only hinted at this in his book, but it seemed the logical conclusion of his theory. In 1871 he made it plain, when he wrote *The Descent of Man, and Selection in Relation to Sex*.

Today, there is overwhelming evidence in favour of Darwin's ideas. Scientists have identified the mechanism by which natural variation occurs and by which inherited characteristics are passed from one generation to the next. It is the complex chemical DNA (deoxyribonucleic acid), which carries information from generation to generation, and strands of which are found in the nucleus of the cells of every living thing.

Natural idea Darwin worked as a naturalist aboard HMS Beagle, during a five-year expedition to South America, which left Britain in 1832. This drawing, by John Gould, is from Darwin's published notes.

MIND BOGGLER
- Unlike other sea creatures, dolphins, whales and porpoises are warm-blooded. They evolved from land-based mammals about 50 million years ago.

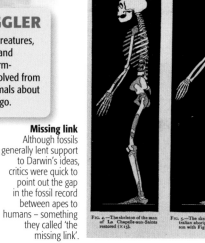

Missing link Although fossils generally lent support to Darwin's ideas, critics were quick to point out the gap in the fossil record between apes to humans – something they called 'the missing link'.

FIG. 4.—The skeleton of the man of La Chapelle-aux-Saints restored (× 15).

FIG. 5.—The skeleton of an tralian aborigine for co on with Fig. 5 (× 15).

Darwin's Bulldog British biologist Thomas Henry Huxley (1825–1895), one of Darwin's supporters. Huxley uncovered evidence supporting the idea that humans and apes are related.

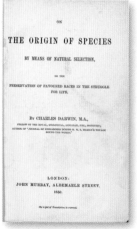

Evolution of an idea The title page of Darwin's book about the origin of species, published in 1859.

WHAT IN THE WORLD?
- **1858** The first aerial photograph is taken from a balloon over Paris, by Gaspard Tournachon (1820–1910).
- **1858** German biologist Rudolph Virchow (1821–1902) correctly suggests that cells arise from existing cells, a new idea at the time.
- **1858** The first transatlantic cable is laid, and the first instant communication between Britain and the USA takes place. The cable deteriorates after only a few days.

NOW JUMP TO... ⊖ DNA page 112; ⊖ ORIGINS OF LIFE page 114

THE Sun

...day, November 25, 1859   Penny farthing

ARE YOU A CHIMP OFF THE OLD BLOCK?
PAGES 12 & 13

MONKEY NUTTER

Barmy boffin Darwin reckons we are all descended from apes

MAD scientist Charles Darwin caused fury last night, claiming we're all descended from APES.

Darwin, 50, makes a string of absurd allegations in his controversial book On The Origin Of Species, published yesterday.

Darwin **SCOFFS** at the "Adam and Eve" theory of mankind's creation. He says the real answer lies in the **FOSSILS** he once studied on a sailing trip. The barmy boffin, from Shrewsbury, reckons

By JEAN POOLE

all animals "evolve" — becoming more and more advanced over thousands of years. This is all thanks to "natural selection" which means only the fittest and best examples of a species survive to breed and pass on their successful traits.

Furious scientists last night insisted Darwin does not have a shred of real evidence. And Church chiefs said he was belittling the Bible and the importance of man over animals.

Baboon Buffoon — Pages 4 & 5

● 65

1862 LOUIS PASTEUR – ENEMY OF GERMS

THE FRENCH chemist and microbiologist Louis Pasteur is best known for making milk, wine and beer safe to drink by killing microbes using heat. The technique, named 'pasteurisation' after him, is still common today. Pasteur's work also highlighted the role of microorganisms in spreading disease and ultimately saved many lives.

In 1856, a brewery asked Pasteur (1822–1895) to find out why so much of its fermenting beer was turning sour. Under the microscope, he saw thousands of microorganisms, or microbes, in the brew. He said they had come from the air and were souring the beer.

Microbes had been observed in pond water as early as 1674, by the Dutch scientist Anton van Leeuwenhoek (1632–1723), but few people considered they might be airborne. Pasteur not only proved they were, but showed they can be killed by heat, by certain chemicals and by passing a liquid through a very fine filter.

From 1862, he developed pasteurisation to protect wine and beer from spoiling. Later, Franz Ritter von Soxlet (1848–1926) used the technique on milk. All of these, when contaminated, had previously been common causes of illness. Pasteur obtained a patent for the process in 1865. Pasteur's research helped him realise the link between microbes and disease. In the

Louis Pasteur, photographed around 1885. As well as his work with pasteurisation, Pasteur found vaccines against anthrax and rabies.

Open and closed Flask and broth used by Pasteur. After heating and sealing the flask, the broth remained unspoiled, unlike similar broth in open containers.

19th century there were several competing theories about the causes of sickness. The most popular blamed 'miasma', supposedly a kind of poisonous vapour produced by decaying matter. The theory dated from the Middle Ages.

The 'germ theory', by contrast, said diseases are caused by microbes. It is still considered valid, although we now know of other things that cause disease, such as prions, which are rogue proteins. Most scientists ridiculed the germ theory, but Pasteur's experiments helped convince many people it was correct.

In 1865, Pasteur devoted his skills and theories to the plight of the silkworm, being devastated by two parasitic microbes and threatening the French silk industry.

One man he influenced was British surgeon Joseph Lister (1827–1912), who was changing the way he carried out operations to cut infection rates. He could not use heat or a filter to combat bacteria during surgery, so he chose chemicals.

Fighting germs Carbolic acid spray from the 1870s, used as an antiseptic in surgery.

Surgical spirit Joseph Lister, pioneer of antiseptic medicine.

MIND BOGGLER

● Around 100 BC, Ancient Roman scholar Marcus Varro (116–27 BC) suggested that disease was caused and passed on by living things too small to see.

Whenever he cut into a person's body he sprayed carbolic acid (phenol) on to the wound to kill microbes. He also made sure he shielded the wound from the air as much as possible.

Lister managed to reduce deaths from infection, or sepsis, from 45 per cent in 1865 to 15 per cent by 1869. Today antiseptics are used to make operating theatres and surgeons free of microbes while surgical instruments are heated to high temperatures to sterilise them.

Many were impressed by Lister's success but still few believed it had anything to do with microbes. However, the germ theory was largely accepted during the 1880s mainly due to German microbiologist Robert Koch (1843–1910), who showed that each disease is caused by a specific microbe. He also took microbes from diseased animals, grew them in the laboratory and transferred them to healthy animals, which developed the same disease.

Today, we realise most microbes are harmless or even beneficial. And thanks largely to Pasteur, Lister and Koch we have more control over harmful ones.

Disease fighter German bacteriologist Robert Koch, pictured around 1890.

WHAT IN THE WORLD?

1859 The first internal combustion engine is made, by Belgian Etienne Lenoir (1822–1900).

1859 Work on the Suez Canal begins.

1859 Gustav Kirchoff (1824–1887) and Robert Bunsen (1811–1899) learn to identify elements from the light they emit when heated (spectroscopy).

1860 Christian von Meyer (1801–1869) discovers the first fossil of *Archaeopteryx*, the dinosaur-like ancestor of birds.

1861 The beginning of the American Civil War (ends in 1865).

1861 Telegraph cables span the whole USA, from New York to San Francisco.

NOW JUMP TO... ◑ MICROSCOPES page 32; ◐ SANITATION page 72

THE Sun

Monday, April 21, 1862 — Penny farthing

Are you maid in heaven?

GET THAT LOOK: SEE PAGE 55

Past its best, Louis . . . Prof hard at work in his lab testing samples of milk

SIP, SIP HOORAY

Genius Pasteur makes milk safe

By GAZ MARKFOUR

MILK will soon be completely safe to drink, it was revealed last night.

A new process dreamed up by scientist Louis Pasteur kills the bacteria which make people ill.

Professor Pasteur, 43, has proved that if you heat milk to as much as 70°C for about half an hour it destroys harmful bugs without damaging the liquid. Better still, the Prof says the process, to be called "Pasteurisation" after him, may well stop **WINE** and **BEER** going off.

A Government spokesman said last night: "If true, his claims will have a major impact on milk drinking."

Pasteur, based in Paris, first found fame when he discovered how bacteria — or "germs" — can produce disease. Pasteur believes many illnesses are caused by these germs entering the body — and hopes to invent various life-saving vaccines.

Incredibly, the selfish French government has first asked him to turn his hand to saving the **SILKWORM**.

Billions of the tiny creatures are dying, threatening the French silk industry, and Pasteur believes a germ is to blame.

Silk Sulk — Page Two

1876 THE TELEPHONE: A KEY BREAKTHROUG

THE TELEPHONE is one of the greatest inventions ever, allowing instant voice communication between people on different sides of the world. The patent granted to Alexander Graham Bell, one of several inventors who raced to perfect it, was the most lucrative in history.

The idea of transmitting the sound of the human voice along electrical wires had been worked on since the 1860s by various inventors, including the American Elisha Gray (1835–1901).

Both he and Bell, a Scot, filed patent applications for the telephone on the same day, February 14, 1876. Bell beat Gray by a couple of hours.

The following month Bell (1847–1922) succeeded for the first time in transmitting intelligible speech – to his assistant in another room. His words, the world's first telephone message, were: 'Mr Watson, come here, I want you.'

Crank call Early telephone with no dial or keypad. Turning the crank handle generated an electric current, which alerted the operator that you wanted to make a call.

Finger work Dial phone, 1930s. Thanks to Almon Strowger's invention of the automatic switchboard, callers could dial telephone numbers direct.

WHAT IN THE WORLD?

1865 Scottish mathematician and physicist James Clerk Maxwell (1831–1879) publishes his equations of electromagnetism, showing that light is a form of electromagnetic radiation.

1865 British surgeon Joseph Lister (1827–1912) begins using carbolic acid antiseptic during surgery.

1865 The Salvation Army is founded.

1865 Lewis Carroll (1832–1898) publishes *Alice's Adventures in Wonderland*.

1869 Russian chemist Dmitri Mendeleev (1834–1907) devises the first modern periodic table of elements.

1873 English astronomer Richard Proctor (1837–1888) correctly suggests that the moon's craters are made by meteorite impact, not volcanoes.

Bell's telephone converted the vibrations which make up human speech into electrical signals and sent them down the wire, while a receiver at the other end converted them back into speech.

In the next few months Bell gave public demonstrations of the technology and made the first long distance calls along existing telegraph cables. In 1877, he set up a company to profit from his invention. The firm soon rented out several phones for use on private lines.

The first exchange opened in 1878, in the U.S. An exchange is essential on a public telephone network. It contains switching equipment that connects the caller's line to that of the person they are phoning. Without one, every house and business would have to be physically connected to every other. Europe's first exchange opened in London in 1879. Early exchanges were staffed by operators who connected lines by pushing plugs into a 'switch board'.

In 1888, American inventor Almon Strowger (1839–1902) devised a way to connect calls automatically without an operator. To call another person, you entered their individual number digit by digit, using a dial. Each digit sent electric pulses down the line which gave the exchange the 'code' to connect to the other person's line. However, many exchanges remained manual until the 1950s.

In the 1970s, telephones and the telephone system began to change significantly. The touch-tone, or keypad, took over from the dial. And most connections between exchanges

Switch bored Telephone operator at Victoria, 1921. Being an operator was sometimes stressful work; it was found that women had more patience than men.

Barbed wire

American farmer Joseph Glidden (1813–1906) patented his design for barbed wire in 1874. His invention was very popular – by the time he died, he was one of the USA's richest people and his wire had transformed the Great Plains and the lives of those living there.

MIND BOGGLER

● The first ever telephone directory was published in New Haven, Connecticut, in February 1878. It listed 21 telephone numbers.

became digital. Devices at the exchange converted the traditional 'analogue' voice signal into digital information. Digital signals can be routed more easily, and millions of calls carried around the world by laser light in a single optical fibre, or by satellite. Even more revolutionary was the invention of the mobile phone, introduced in the USA in the 1970s and popular in Britain from the late 1980s.

Today, many people make telephone and even video calls via the Internet. The technology is called 'voice over IP' (IP stands for 'Internet Protocol'). Calls are not routed through the traditional telephone line at all.

On the move Early mobile phone, 1985, designed for the busy executive, for use in the car or on foot. The large black box is the battery pack.

NOW JUMP TO... ◀ TELEGRAPH page 60; ▶ RADIO page 80; ▶ THE INTERNET page 128

THE Sun

nday, June 26, 1876   1½d

HERE'S how the "phone" could look, installed in the home.

The caller speaks into a box on the wall, which acts as the transmitter and is powered by electricity.

Then he listens to the response on a hand-held receiver pressed to his ear.

One day most homes may have one.

arp . . . barbed wire

sh for
arbed
e' set
kill off
wboy

DWARD IMAM

YS in the Wild
were fearing for
obs last night
e of the rapid
p of the new
d" wire.

decades land-
have employed
to patrol the
e boundaries of
roperty on the
pen ranges of
eat Plains.

horsemen keep
oss's cattle on
operty and other
FF.

the new wire,
has vicious
and is the first
ccessfully keep
in an enclosure,
set to make the
redundant.

disconsolate
told The Sun:
pardner . . .
ouzzard food."

OOS
N'T
OD
e Page 2

Hello. . . hello?
Bell shows off his
phone yesterday

LORD OF THE RINGS

Inventor called Bell unveils amazing 'telephone'

From **DI LINGTONE** and **FERN YERMUM** in Philadelphia

AN amazing gadget unveiled yesterday could soon allow a person to talk to a friend in a different house.

The "telephone" can already transmit the sound of a voice from one room to the next.

And Scottish inventor Alexander Graham Bell reckons it could be used over much longer distances.

The telephone involves a transmitter and receiver. Words spoken into the transmitter travel along a wire and are heard in the receiver.

The gizmo has caused a sensation at a Philadelphia exhibition. Bell said: "The day will come when friends converse with each other without leaving home."

My Ding-a-ling — Page Two

Give us a Bell . . . inventor's first model. He has since refined it

1880 THOMAS EDISON: PROLIFIC INVENTOR

THOMAS Alva Edison is the most prolific inventor in history – a remarkable man whose refinement of the light bulb ushered in the age of electricity.

Edison (1847–1931), a shrewd American businessman as well as an inventor, ended up with more than 1,000 patents to his name. Most of his inventions were developed under his direction by a team at the world's first research and development facility, which he set up at Menlo Park, New Jersey, USA.

The Menlo Park complex was made possible by income generated by one of Edison's earliest successes – the quadruplex telegraph, a device that allowed four messages to be sent simultaneously along a single cable. His other early hit was the stock ticker, which printed out share prices direct from the stock exchange, via telegraph.

Among his most famous inventions was the phonograph, the first sound recording device, comprising a cylinder wrapped in tinfoil into which a stylus would cut grooves. It caused disbelief when he first showed it off. One scientist declared it a ventriloquist's trick. Other Edison triumphs included the kinetoscope, a stand-alone device for watching short films in amusement arcades, and an improved microphone for early telephones.

Some of his inventions were not entirely new. In many cases, he and his team simply made an existing idea more practical and commercially viable. The light bulb is a good example. It had been known for decades that electric current can heat metal to a temperature high enough to make it glow – a phenomenon called incandescence. Within months of the invention of the battery in 1800, scientists had seen this glow as current passed through very thin strips of metal. They saw the potential of electric lighting, but the hot metal reacted with air and soon burned through.

For decades, inventors tried to find a way around this problem. Putting the metal in a sealed glass 'bulb' and removing the air seemed to help – but hot metal evaporates in a vacuum, so this did not work for long either. Using thin strips of bamboo or paper coated with carbon was better, and cheaper.

English physicist and chemist Joseph Swan (1828–1914) made a successful light bulb using carbon-coated paper in the 1860s, but vacuum pumps at the time were not strong enough to remove all the air, so the carbon would sometimes catch fire. He improved his design in the 1870s, with a 'carbonised' cotton filament and a better vacuum pump, and took out a patent in Britain in 1878 – a year before Edison did so in the USA.

Edison's team improved the electric light. In 1879, their bulbs typically lasted for 1,800 hours. Until then, no one had made one lasting more than 15 hours. Edison's were also cheap, to encourage people to buy into the other vital ingredient of electric lighting, electric power. Edison formed the Edison Electric Illuminating Company, which opened the world's second public power station at Pearl Street, New York in 1882. (The first was in Godalming, Surrey.)

Electrification took decades to complete. But eventually electric lighting took over from gas, which had been in widespread use since the early 19th century. In the 1850s, there were 1,000 gasworks in Britain alone, the gas produced by heating coal. In the 1930s, natural gas began to replace coal gas. Natural gas remains a popular fuel for cooking and heating today – and for generating electricity, in gas-fired power stations.

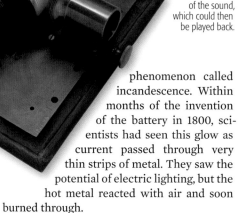
Tin drum Edison's phonograph, 1877 – the first sound recording device. Sound made a stylus vibrate, which made indentations in the tinfoil cylinder. As the cylinder rotated, it recorded the vibrations of the sound, which could then be played back.

MIND BOGGLER
● On October 21, 1931, a few days after Edison died, millions of people across the USA dimmed their lights for one minute in tribute.

WHAT IN THE WORLD?
1877 German-born inventor Emile Berliner (1851–1929) invents the microphone.
1877 The first ever cricket Test between England and Australia.
1877 American astronomer Asaph Hall (1829–1907) discovers the two moons of Mars, later named Phobos and Diemos.
1878 The first public telephone exchange opens, in New Haven, Connecticut, USA.
1879 Louis Pasteur (1822–1895) discovers a vaccine against cholera (in chickens), the second vaccine ever used – the first was against smallpox.

A different light Joseph Swan's patented light bulb, 1878. The blackening was caused by carbon from the hot filament being deposited on the inside of the glass. From 1903, the metal tungsten was used to make light bulb filaments.

Moving image Edison's kinetoscope, 1894. Looking in through the viewing angle and turning a handle, you could see a looped 20-second film.

Spark of an idea Edison's steam-powered dynamo, at the world's second power station, in New York. It produced 115 volts, and served 59 homes and businesses.

NOW JUMP TO... ➲ SLICED BREAD page 98; ➲ CINEMA page 76

THE Sun

dnesday, January 28, 1880   1½d

GAS 'IS DOOMED'

By FLEUR ESCENT

GAS lamps, which have lit streets and homes for hundreds of years, could become a thing of the past, it was predicted last night.

One energy expert said: "Obviously, Edison's hardly got any customers yet. But gas is messy and expensive . . . it's hard to imagine it still being around in 100 years if people get into electricity and the price falls."

THE FUTURE'S BRIGHT (Well, brightish)

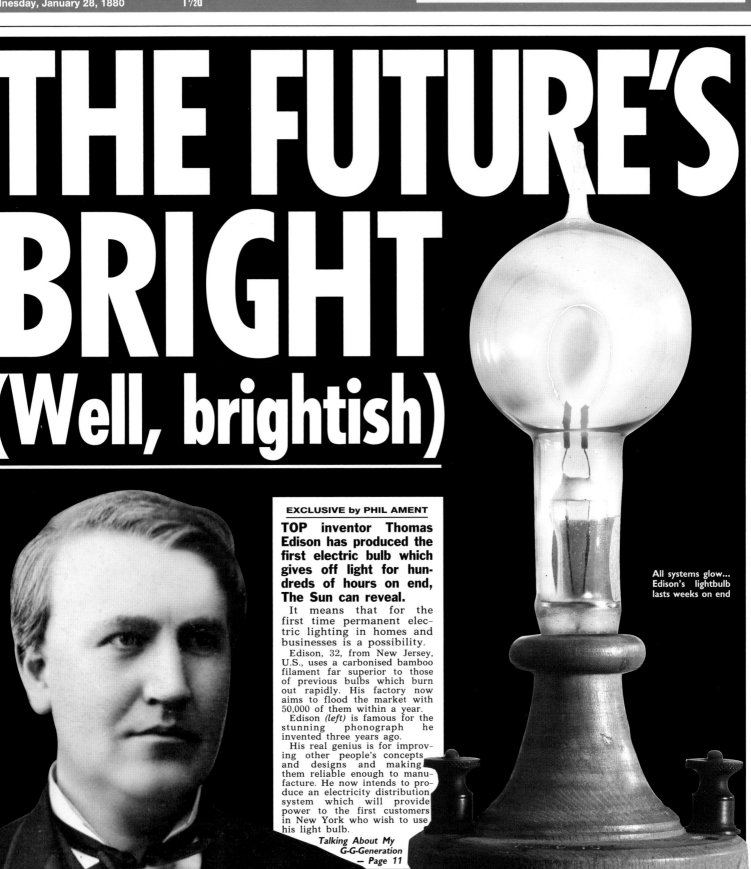

All systems glow...
Edison's lightbulb
lasts weeks on end

EXCLUSIVE by PHIL AMENT

TOP inventor Thomas Edison has produced the first electric bulb which gives off light for hundreds of hours on end, The Sun can reveal.

It means that for the first time permanent electric lighting in homes and businesses is a possibility.

Edison, 32, from New Jersey, U.S., uses a carbonised bamboo filament far superior to those of previous bulbs which burn out rapidly. His factory now aims to flood the market with 50,000 of them within a year.

Edison *(left)* is famous for the stunning phonograph he invented three years ago.

His real genius is for improving other people's concepts and designs and making them reliable enough to manufacture. He now intends to produce an electricity distribution system which will provide power to the first customers in New York who wish to use his light bulb.

*Talking About My
G-G-Generation
— Page 11*

● 71

1881 FLUSHING TOILETS & PUBLIC HYGIENE

CONTRARY to popular myth, Thomas Crapper did not invent the flushing toilet. But he did make one big improvement to it – and made it much more popular – at a time when public health was a major concern.

Cut away One of the plans drawn by engineer Joseph Bazalgette, in the 1860s, for London's Embankment. The sewer runs alongside the river. You can also see the tunnel for London's underground Metropolitan Railway.

Over London by Rail, 1872. Wood engraving by Gustave Dore (1832-1883), showing men and women in the grim and densely-packed tenements of London in 1872.

Venn diagrams

Deceptively simple, Venn diagrams are used to help visualise logical problems in a branch of mathematics known as 'set theory'. They were introduced by English mathematician John Venn (1834–1923).

Until the Industrial Revolution began around 1760, most of Britain's cities were of a manageable size. People tended to live rural lives, working on farms or running their own smallholdings. But the rise of large factories and mills attracted people into cities at an incredible rate. City populations typically trebled or quadrupled in 50 years. By the time Queen Victoria (1819–1901) came to the throne in 1837, cities were noisy, filthy and overcrowded.

Supplying water to big cities is a major technological challenge. By the end of the 18th century, most had pipes bringing in water from nearby springs or rivers. By the middle of the 19th century, steam-powered pumping stations had opened in some cities, with engines lifting water from rivers into towers, from where gravity would deliver water under pressure to thousands of homes.

But as cities grew more crowded, springs could no longer cope and the increasing sewage output inevitably found its way into the water supply. Most people in big cities were poor and lived in terraced slums. Their toilets were pots they emptied into open sewers in the streets or small outside 'closets' above cesspits. Despite the rapid scientific advances of the 18th century, city dwellers in the 19th century were at greater risk of disease than people before industrialisation.

One of the biggest killers was cholera. Between 1830 and 1850 it claimed more than 30,000 lives in London alone. In 1850, London's Metropolitan Commission of Sewers ordered all cesspits closed, wrongly believing cholera was transmitted through the air by a 'dirty vapour' called miasma.

In 1854, English doctor John Snow (1813–1858) proved that cholera is carried in water (we now know it to be caused by a waterborne microbe). After another outbreak killed 10,000 people in 1856, a plan was hatched to build an extensive network of underground sewers in London. The chief engineer was Joseph Bazalgette (1819–1891). He built about 1,700 kilometres (1,000 miles) of pipes from London's streets to the Thames Embankment and 140 kilometres (82 miles) of sewers along the Embankment. All of London's sewage was emptied into the river further downstream. By the end of the 19th century, those sewers empt tied into treatment works rather than straigh into the river.

Thomas Crapper (1836–1910), an English businessman and a plumber by trade, formed hi company in London in 1861 when Bazalgette's sewers were not finished and water supplies patchy and unreliable. Few people needed domestic plumbing. But by the 1880s, things had improved – in London and most large cities. Many families had water tanks in the roo directly filled by filtered water supplies. At last flushing toilets could slot into place: there was a water supply to feed the cisterns, and some where for the waste to go.

Crapper's toilets were state-of-the-art. Although the idea of flushing had been around for centuries, even the most modern systems were weak and prone to leaks. Crapper's 'syphonic flush' was powerful and his toilets well-built.

MIND BOGGLER
● The words 'crap' and 'Crapper' have no connection. 'Crap' has a long history in the English language and remained popular in the American colonies to mean defecation. It was a bizarre coincidence Thomas Crapper should become a champion of the flushing toilet.

Old flush Early flush toilet design, from 1775, by English inventor Joseph Bramah (1749–1814). Pulling the handle released the contents of the bowl into a cesspit or sewer, and simultaneously opened a valve in an overhead cistern, releasing a flush.

WHAT IN THE WORLD?
1879 The Tay Bridge in Dundee collapses. 80 people die and a train ends up in the river.
1880 First cash register is made in America.
1880 Robert Koch starts using solid gel (agar) for growing bacterial colonies.

Flushed with success Page from Thomas Crapper's 1902 catalogue. Crapper promoted and improved the flush toilet.

NOW JUMP TO… ◐ PASTEUR page 66; ◑ PENICILLIN page 104

THE Sun

uesday, October 11, 1881   1½d

ROYAL WEE

EXC-LOO-SIVE by JAMES RIDDLE and LOU ROLLS

PRINCE Edward has ordered THIRTY of the new luxury flushing toilets for Sandringham.

He has engaged top WC-makers Thomas Crapper and Co to supply the conveniences *(left)*, with cedar seats and enclosures, for the Norfolk residence.

The genius of Crapper's lavatory is the "syphonic flush" mechanism which releases the entire contents of a cistern into the pan at once to clean it out.

Previous, rudimentary flushing toilets have relied on the inadequate mains pressure in the average home.

The Royal commission is a triumph for Mr Crapper. He has been a plumber since 1847, when as a lad of 11 he walked 165 miles from Yorkshire to become an apprentice in London.

●Vulgar Americans have used the word "crap" for decades to mean defecation. Last night there were fears they may use this unhappy coincidence to dub Mr Crapper's toilets "crappers."

Flushed With Pride — Page 5

Bowled over . . . toilet boss Crapper

Prince Ed installs 30 Crapper toilets at Sandringham

1886 BENZ AND THE RISE OF THE MOTOR CAR

THE FIRST commercially available automobile looked more like a child's tricycle than a car. But it was the beginning of a transport revolution which would shape the modern world, transforming the landscape and dictating how cities and their suburbs are built. It has come at a price – in environmental damage, crime and road deaths.

It is perhaps no surprise that the first motorcar, the Benz Patent Motorwagen, looks like a tricycle. Cycles had been a childhood passion of German motoring pioneer Karl Benz (1844–1929). In adulthood, he grew interested in the internal combustion engine – which was to be the dominant engine technology.

Until the 1860s nearly all engines – including those in prototype cars – were steam-driven. Combustion, normally of coal, took place continuously in a furnace outside the cylinder. In an internal combustion engine, gas, petrol or diesel burns inside the cylinder. The combustion takes place under pressure, very quickly and repeatedly, as a series of mini-explosions. The resulting hot gases push directly on the cylinder.

The first practical internal combustion engines were made by Belgian engineer Etienne Lenoir (1822–1900) in 1859. They were basic and lacked power but were reliable and much more convenient than steam engines. Lenoir sold a few hundred engines, which were used to power small machines such as printing presses and water pumps.

German inventor Nikolaus Otto (1832–1891)

created an improved internal combustion engine in 1876. This was a four-stroke engine with a single cylinder. The piston's movements helped suck petrol in and push exhaust gases out. The four repeating stages were intake, compression, power and exhaust – still the basic design of most standard petrol engines in cars.

Benz formed a company in 1883 and made his own engine based on Otto's design. By 1885 he had designed and built his first Motorwagen. He was granted a patent and after making a few modifications began selling the car in 1888. By 1893, he had sold 25.

Motoring had a long way to go before it became convenient or even popular. At the time Benz produced his first cars, petrol was only available from the chemist, as a cleaning fluid. The first cars had to be pushed to get uphill and were unaffordable for all but the very rich.

On the road Motoring enthusiast Charles Rolls (1877–1910) driving his first car in 1896. Before that year, motorists were limited to 4 miles per hour in the country and 2 miles per hour in town, and they had to make sure that someone was walking in front of them with a flag or lantern.

But cars did promise convenience and independence, and would eventually rid the streets of horse manure and the clatter of hooves and cartwheels.

It took the entrepreneurial talents of American industrialist Henry Ford (1863–1947) to bring cars to a wider public. In 1908, the first of a new generation of cars rolled off Ford's production line in Detroit, USA. It was the 'Model T', which was also made in factories in Manchester, England, and mainland Europe. By the time the last Model T was produced in 1927, Ford had sold more than 15 million.

Now, more than 120 years after Benz's Motorwagen made its debut, cars are the world's primary means of transportation, with more than half a BILLION on the planet's roads.

Look inside The piston is visible inside this cutaway four-cylinder, four-stroke Ader engine from 1903. At the top of each cylinder, you can see a spark plug.

Model T Ford Like all model T Ford cars produced after 1913, this one is black.

MIND BOGGLER

● The car has come a long way since's Benz's debut. The Bugatti Veyron costs $1.2million, has a top speed of 230mph and goes from 0-62 in 2.5 seconds. It is the dearest factory-built car ever.

WHAT IN THE WORLD?

1881 The first electric tram, in Berlin.
1881 German biologist Paul Ehrlich finds a way of staining bacteria to make them more visible and help identify them.
1882 The world's first hydroelectric power plant opens, in the USA.
1883 The volcanic island of Krakatoa explodes, killing 40,000 people.
1883 Robert Koch (1843–1910) discovers the bacterium that causes cholera.
1884 Anglo-Irish engineer Charles Parsons (1854–1931) designs and installs the first steam turbines for generating electricity.
1884 Swedish chemist Svante Arrhenius (1859–1927) introduces the ionic theory of solutions.
1885 Gottlieb Daimler (1834–1900) builds the world's first motorcycle.

Lenoir gas engine, 1860 – the first practical internal combustion engine. The large flywheel is obvious, but you can also see electric batteries to produce a spark inside the cylinder.

NOW JUMP TO... ◀ STEPHENSON'S ROCKET page 56; ▶ POWERED FLIGHT page 84

THE Sun

Monday, July 5, 1886   1½d

STEER WE GO

First pic of Benz car

THIS is the first picture of Karl Benz's amazing horseless carriage.

Crowds watched in awe at the weekend as the engine-powered three-wheeled "motorcar" was driven through Mannheim, Germany.

German engineer Benz, 41, has built the vehicle with solid rub-

By REGGIE STRATION, Transport Editor

ber tyres and a plush leather seat big enough for two.

It has one of his own-design internal-combustion engines which run on petroleum.

This is placed over the rear axle and makes the wheels spin using a belt and chain. A lever attached to the front wheel enables the driver to steer. The

engine is about one horsepower and the whole contraption zips along at a top speed of about 9mph.

A Health Department spokesman said last night: "It'll make life so much better and cleaner when everyone has one of these.

"At the moment we have horse dung all over the streets – plus, it takes ages to get anywhere."

All The Rage On The Road — Page 7

e's no fuel . . .
arl Benz's car
is a sensation

1895 MOVIES: BIRTH OF AN ARTFORM

MOVING images are everywhere today – on TV, at the cinema, on computers and now on mobile phones. Films are big business, and one of the world's most vibrant art forms. It is hard to believe it is little more than 100 years since the first cinema screening.

The birth of the cinema is down to French inventors Auguste and Louis Lumière (1862–1954 and 1864–1948), who patented an ingenious device called the Cinématographe in February 1895. It was a movie camera, printer and projector all in one. With it, they captured and projected short, simple documentaries.

The Lumières' first public screening was on December 28th 1895 at the Grand Café in Paris. Their short film 'L'arrivée d'un train en gare de la Ciotat' (The Arrival of a Train at Ciotat Station) showed the engine chugging towards the screen. The story that the audience panicked and fled is often repeated – but it is now thought unlikely the Parisians were unsophisticated enough to have been taken in. After Paris, the Lumières put on shows in London, New York and Bombay in 1896.

Moving pictures are an illusion. Although they are a sequence of still images taken a fraction of a second apart, the brain convinces us we are seeing continuous movement. The first device to take advantage of this was the thaumatrope, a popular Victorian toy comprising a card with a different picture on either side which was flicked round at high speed to produce the illusion of one moving image. A more advanced version of the principle was the zoetrope, a spinning cylinder with slits in the sides which conjured the illusion of action from the rapid sequence of still pictures inside.

Moving pictures were only made possible through advances in photography in the late 1800s. Before the 1870s, each photograph needed a few

Lumière Cinematographe no 8, 1896 One of 200 cinématographes made for the Lumière brothers in 1896, after the success of their film shows.

Motion pictures The zoetrope, invented in the 1830s, contains a sequence pictures on the inside. Look through the slits as the drum spins, and the sequence appears to move.

seconds' exposure – besides which no camera existed that could take pictures in quick succession. When these hurdles were overcome, there was one more problem: photographs were still taken on heavy glass plates.

In 1889, George Eastman (1854–1932) pioneered celluloid film, ideal for a movie camera. It is transparent, durable and flexible, and sprocket holes can be punched in it so the movie camera mechanism can precisely move the film frame-by-frame.

Although the Lumières were the first to screen movies to a paying public they were not the first to capture them. The two brothers were inspired by the kinetoscope, which its inventor Thomas Edison (1847–1931) unveiled in 1893. It was a stand-alone viewer that showed short films in amusement arcades.

The Lumières eventually decided films had little future and returned to photography. But movies really caught the public's imagination. In the early 1900s, film-makers began to use special

Film studio Probably the first purpose-built film studio was Edison's 'Black Maria' studio, in New Jersey, USA. It was operational from 1893 until 1901, and hundreds of short films were made there.

Still pictures In the late 1870s, English photographer Edweard Muybridge (1830-1904) took sequences of photographs like this, by triggering lines of stills cameras. He could project the images one after the other, to give the impression of movement.

MIND BOGGLER
● The 1997 movie *Titanic* is easily the biggest box office hit of all time, with a worldwide gross of $1,845,034,188. *Gone With The Wind* (1939) sold more tickets, but the receipts were much lower because prices were too.

effects, editing and creative lighting. The earliest 'cinemas' were set up in converted shops, fairground tents and music halls.

By the early 1920s, film-making was a boom industry, with thousands of purpose-built cinemas showing full-length silent features, whose leading actors became huge stars. Most cinemas featured a live organist, pianist or small band to create mood music. Sound was introduced in the late 1920s. Hollywood, a district of Los Angeles, became the centre for movie studios and stars. Colour film was introduced in the 1930s and eventually became the norm.

Since then, television and video, and more recently digitised video on DVD and the Internet, have brought new ways of experiencing moving pictures.

NOW JUMP TO... ● PHOTOGRAPHY page 54; ● TELEVISION page 94

THE Sun

Monday, December 30, 1895 NOW ONLY 1d

IS LOCO FILM TOO STEAMY FOR OUR KIDS?
VIEW THE JURY — Page 8

HORROR 'MOVIE'

Panic as film of speeding train is screened

'No future' . . . Lumieres

A TERRIFIED theatre audience fled from a "film" of a moving train — because they thought the loco would run them over.

The Paris crowd were

By OSCAR WINNER

panicked by the footage of the engine steaming towards the camera.

Brothers Auguste and Louis Lumiere made it with the "cinematograph" they have invented to record and project

moving images. One witness said: "There was fear, terror, even panic."

Despite the emotion the film stirred up, the French brothers reckon there is no future in "cinema" and want to concentrate on photography.

So far they have made several films of everyday events

— but doubt people will pay to watch something they can see for nothing in the street.

The Lumieres once worked for their dad's photographic firm and want to return to it.

One industry insider said: "You can't help feeling they're being a bit hasty."

That's a Wrap — Page 5

● 77

1896 X-RAYS: NEW ERA FOR MEDICINE & PHYSICS

THE discovery of the X-ray was met with great excitement around the world, having obvious benefits for medicine as well as opening up an exciting new branch of physics.

German physicist Wilhelm Röntgen (1845–1923) discovered X-rays in 1895 while experimenting with electric discharges in glass tubes.

Working in the dark, he noticed a faint glow on a screen nearby – the screen was made of a mineral known to glow when ultraviolet radiation falls on it. Röntgen realised that the tube was producing invisible rays but he knew they could not be ultraviolet radiation because the tube was covered in thick cardboard. Even more intriguingly, when he put the screen in a cupboard it continued to glow, but only when the tube was switched on.

Röntgen investigated the effect day and night for weeks, and discovered that his strange rays pass through more materials than light does but are blocked by most dense materials. Röntgen discovered early on that he could record X-rays and their shadows on photographic paper, and became the first to take X-ray photographs. He found out that his rays pass through flesh, but not bones, and quickly realised the medical potential of that.

X-ray tube The screw end of this 1920s X-ray tube was connected to the negative side of a high voltage electrical supply. The other end was connected to the positive side. When the supply was turned on, electrons were pulled at high speed from the small black cylinder onto the angled plate. The electrons released their energy as X-rays. Modern tubes work in the same way.

Röntgen did not know what his rays were, so named his discovery after the 'x' in algebra that represents an unknown quantity. Most other scientists at the time called them 'Röntgen rays'. Soon after Röntgen published details of his experiment, other physicists realised the mystery rays were another form of electromagnetic radiation. Physicists knew several already: light, ultraviolet radiation, infrared radiation and radio waves. The only difference between these various forms of electromagnetic radiation is the frequency – how fast the radiation oscillates as it passes through space. Ultraviolet radiation had the highest known frequencies, and radio waves the lowest. Physicists had been waiting for a form of radiation with frequencies higher than ultraviolet radiation – and Röntgen had found it.

The discovery of X-rays heralded the beginning of a new and exciting era of physics. Within a few months, French chemist Henri Becquerel (1852–1908) discovered another form of electromagnetic radiation with even higher frequencies. These were gamma rays, produced by 'radioactive' materials. Becquerel also found two other forms of radioactive rays that are not electromagnetic radiation. Physicists were soon using Becquerel's rays to probe the inner workings of atoms.

And in 1897, English physicist Joseph John Thomson (1856–1940) made the bold suggestion that the stream of particles passing through glass vacuum tubes was carried by 'corpuscles' which could be smaller than atoms. These were later called electrons.

X-rays are still widely used today. Probably their most common use is in medicine, where they are particularly useful for analysing bone defects, but can also detect growths and blockages.

MIND BOGGLER

● Thomas Edison developed glass tubes to produce X-rays for medical purposes. But such was the naivety about the dangers of X-rays that one of his glassblowers repeatedly tested the tubes on his hands – contracting a cancer so vicious that doctors amputated both arms in a vain bid to save his life.

Alfred Nobel

Swedish chemist Alfred Nobel (1833–1896) amassed a huge fortune mostly as a result of his invention of dynamite in 1867. He never married, and was a bit of a recluse. Stung by criticism of his work, he left the bulk of his wealth in trust to fund annual awards for excellence: the Nobel Prizes, first awarded in 1901.

Nobel wanted five prizes: for Physics, Chemistry, Physiology or Medicine, Literature and Peace. In 1969, the Bank of Sweden added a sixth for Economic Science. The prizes are given to those people judged to have given the greatest benefit to the human race. The prestige and the financial reward for winning one are considerable.

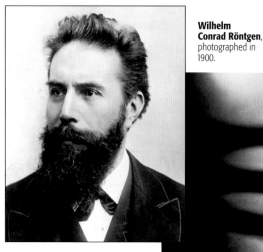

Wilhelm Conrad Röntgen, photographed in 1900.

Another winner Nobel Prize medal. JJ Thomson won the Physics prize in 1906, for his 1897 discovery of the electron.

All in hand This is the first X-ray photograph, taken in December 1895, by Röntgen. It shows his wife's hand – and the ring on her finger.

WHAT IN THE WORLD?

1895 Dutch anatomist Eugene Dubois (1858–1940) brings back fossils of *Homo erectus*, an ancient 'ape man', from the Indonesian island of Java.

1895 Rugby league is founded in Huddersfield.

1895 Karl Benz (1844–1929) produces the first lorry.

NOW JUMP TO... ◆ **GUNPOWDER page 20;** ◆ **CURIE page 90**

THE Sun

day, December 11, 1896   1d

PAGE 3
X-POSED

Our stunners as you've NEVER seen them before

NEXT week The Sun launches the most in-depth look at our Page 3 stunners EVER.

Thanks to the wonders of X-rays, discovered last year by German scientist Wilhelm Röntgen, you'll find out:

By SEYMOUR JOINTS

●The intimate secrets only their osteopaths can possibly know.

●What REALLY tickles their funny bones.

●If their knee bones really ARE connected to their thigh bones. Never before have our girls been so transparently open about themselves.

Make no bones about it, it's the best Page 3 series yet. You'd be out of your skull to miss it.

MR DYNAMITE IS DEAD
Nobel millions to fund annual prizes

Nobel . . . out with a bang

By SAUL OVER, Obituaries Editor

THE inventor of dynamite died last night, leaving his fortune to fund prizes for science, literature and peace.

Alfred Nobel made at least $4million from explosives.

But the 63-year-old Swede was shamed into creating the annual prizes when a critic claimed he would only be remembered for "becoming rich by finding ways to kill more people faster than ever."

Full Explosives Story — Page 17

1897 TURNING POINT FOR COMMUNICATIONS

RADIO communications are used to broadcast terrestrial and satellite radio and television as well as mobile phone signals. They were pioneered by a brilliant young Italian, Guglielmo Marconi, who made Britain his home.

Radio waves are produced whenever an electric current flows to-and-fro. They travel out in all directions at 300,000 kilometres per second (186,000 miles per second), the speed of light. In modern communications, radio waves are produced by currents in wires called antennas. But the first radio waves made deliberately were produced by electric current jumping through the air as a spark.

Scottish physicist James Clerk Maxwell (1831–1879) predicted the existence of radio waves in 1864 after working out the mathematical relationship between electric and magnetic fields. But German physicist Heinrich Hertz (1857–1894) was first to prove they exist, in a remarkable experiment in 1888. Hertz made a spark jump the gap between two metal electrodes, producing a burst of radio waves. He set up a similar gap 1.5 metres (5 feet) away, which was connected to a battery and on the verge of sparking. When the radio waves from the first gap reached the second gap, they caused a spark there. The second spark always followed immediately after the first – showing a radio signal was passing 'wirelessly' through the air.

Marconi (1874–1937) was the man who set up the world's first radio stations to broadcast 'wireless telegraphy' – bursts of radio waves sent across large distances, carrying Morse code. He began experimenting with radio in Italy in 1894, reproducing and improving Hertz's experiment. By attaching one end of each spark gap to a long wire, he made the apparatus much more sensitive – he had made the world's first antennas. Marconi extended the distance across which he could detect the radio waves – first to 9 metres (30 feet), then to 2.4 kilometres (1.5 miles). He

Spark gap Marconi's first beam transmitter. A spark produced across the gap produced radio waves, which reflected off the metal dish behind, producing a beam.

Flying high Artwork showing the antenna used by Marconi in Newfoundland to receive the first transatlantic radio signals, in 1901.

replaced the spark gaps with a more sensitive device called a 'coherer' and began sending messages as on-and-off pulses of Morse code.

In 1896 Marconi moved to England where he soon impressed executives of the Post Office and the Army with demonstrations on Salisbury Plain, Wiltshire, and across the Channel. In 1901 he managed to send a message across the Atlantic, from Cornwall to Newfoundland, now in Canada. He received the Nobel Prize for Physics in 1909.

In 1906 American inventor Lee de Forest (1873–1961) invented an electronic gadget called the Audion which enabled engineers to produce radio waves of pure frequencies and manipulate them to carry sound rather than just Morse code. It was not

NOW JUMP TO... ❸ **TELEGRAPH page 60;** ❸ **TELEPHONE page 68;** ❸ **TELEVISION page 94**

Guinea pigs

We often use the term 'guinea pig' to mean a person taking part in an experiment. But real guinea pigs were used for the first time in the late 19th century. In 1882, Robert Koch (1843–1910) used them in experiments to find the microbes responsible for cholera. Today, rats and mice are used much more often than guinea pigs; they reproduce more quickly and are physiologically more like humans.

until 1915 that radio engineers were transmitting sound effectively, however.

The transistor was invented in 1948. It does the same thing as the Audion but is much smaller and uses less power. The transistor made radio receivers more portable. Today, most of the manipulation of radio signals is done on miniature circuits on microchips.

Turn it down Valve radio receiver, 1920s. Lee de Forest's Audion provided a means for amplification, and was commonly known as the 'valve'. Most electronic devices had valves until the invention of the transistor in 1948.

MIND BOGGLER

● More than a century after Marconi's breakthrough, NASA's navigators are sending instructions to the robot probes exploring Mars using high-frequency radio waves.

Listening in From the 1920s, radio became a way in which the public could be entertained and informed. This family, photographed in 1945, is listening in to a broadcast by Winston Chruchill (1874–1965).

THE Sun

ursday, March 18, 1897 1d

RADIO HEAD

genius sends signal 4 miles through thin air

My boxes of tricks... Marconi toying with his gadgets last night

A MAN of 22 made history yesterday by sending a radio signal FOUR MILES.

Bigwigs from the Post Office, the Army and the Navy watched agog as Guglielmo

EXCLUSIVE by ROGER NOUT

Marconi performed the stunt on Salisbury Plain, Wilts.

Italian-born Marconi sent out a Morse Code signal on the "airwaves", picking up the transmission

using an aerial fixed to a balloon for extra height.

Incredibly the young inventor reckons he may eventually be able to send signals across the **ATLANTIC.**

That would mean a revolution in worldwide communications – and allow ships to talk to each other at

sea. Marconi has dabbled with radio since his teens and now has the heavyweight backing of Post Office chief engineer Sir William Preece.

One observer said: "What he's done is simply incredible, especially considering his age."

Radio Won-derful — Page 11

1903 ROCKETS: A VISION OF SPACE FLIGHT

ROCKETS had been used on the battlefield for hundreds of years before Konstantin Tsiolkovsky dreamed of the possibility of space flight. But in working out how they could thrust people upwards, above Earth's atmosphere and off to other planets, he was decades ahead of his time.

Rockets are pushed forwards by gases escaping from the back at high speed. In rockets used on the battlefield and in space travel, these gases are the result of rapid burning of fuel.

The earliest rockets were fire arrows used in China in the 11th century, and although early rockets were very inaccurate they were commonplace in battles in Europe from the 14th century.

English inventor William Congreve (1772–1828) created a more accurate battlefield rocket in the early 19th century, with an improved launcher and a long stick for guidance. Another English inventor, William

> **MIND BOGGLER**
> ● The massive Saturn V used in the Apollo programme is the biggest rocket in history, more than 363ft (110.6m) high and 33ft (10m) in diameter with a total mass of more than 3,000 tons. It was almost as tall as St Paul's Cathedral in London.

Rocket man Robert Goddard, photographed just before the first lift-off of the first ever liquid fuel rocket, in 1926.

Hale (1797–1870), made war rockets much more accurate in 1844 by making them spin as they flew.

Thanks to advances in astronomy, people in the 19th century had a reasonable knowledge of the stars and planets, and the enormous distances between them and Earth. Tsiolkovsky (1857–1935), a partially deaf Russian maths teacher, was fascinated by it all. He was the first person to suggest humans might one day populate the rest of the solar system and beyond.

Long before the technology existed to make any of it possible, Tsiolkovsky immersed himself in the technical details of space flight, including multi-stage rockets, space stations and airlocks for leaving spacecraft to go on space walks. He correctly worked out that a rocket would need to travel at 8 kilometres per second (18,000 mph) to escape Earth's atmosphere and realised that liquid fuel, rather than solid, was the likely way to achieve it. Tsiolkovsky is most unlikely to have made the pages of The *Sun*, however, since it was decades before his ideas were published outside the then Soviet Union, where he was held in great esteem, receiving a state funeral in 1935.

Unaware of Tsiolkovsky's ideas, American Robert Goddard (1882–1945) became the first person to experiment practically with liquid fuel rockets. He succeeded in 1926 with a flight that lasted a few seconds and only climbed to 13 metres (15 yards). From this humble beginning, Goddard developed faster, more powerful rockets with guidance systems, and which rose about 1.6 kilometres (1 mile).

In 1923 an Austrian scientist called Hermann Oberth (1894–1989) published *By Rocket Into Interplanetary Space*. This book inspired enthusiasts including Wernher von Braun to experiment with liquid-fuelled rockets. Von Braun went on to work for the German army and led development of the V-2 rockets,

Spinning weapon Rocket designed by William Hale. Exhaust gases expelled at the back of the rocket hit the three angled fins, causing the rocket to spin. This made Hale rockets very stable in flight.

Launch pad Frame for launching rockets designed by William Congreve. Notice the long stick, which made these rockets fly straighter than previous designs.

Flying machine?

A few people had lifted off for a few seconds before the Wright Brothers' famous flight of 1903 – but nothing more than long hops. English-born New Zealand inventor Richard Pearse (1877–1953) may however have beaten the Wrights to the first sustained, powered flight. Eyewitness accounts suggest he achieved flights of several hundred metres. But no photographs exist, and the evidence is generally inconclusive.

thousands of which were fired from occupied Europe at England during the war.

At the end of the war, German rocket specialists and unused equipment fell into Allied hands and formed the basis of fledgling post war space programmes in Russia and the USA.

The Russians eventually won the race to put the first man into orbit. He was Yuri Gagarin sent up in 1961 by a team of engineers and designers inspired by more than 500 scientific papers written by space visionary Konstantin Tsiolkovsky.

Flying terror This V-2 rocket was captured and brought to Britain after World War II. Between 1942 and 1945, more than 3,000 of these rockets were fired at Britain and the Low Countries.

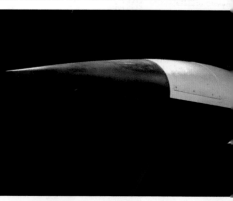

WHAT IN THE WORLD?

1897 British physicist JJ Thomson (1856–1940) discovers the electron.

1899 Marie Curie (1867–1934) renames Becquerel's uranium rays 'radioactivity' after she and her husband find them coming from another element, thorium.

1900 German physicist Max Planck (1858–1947) takes the first step towards 'quantum theory', by postulating that energy can only be transferred in certain amounts.

1901 Austrian doctor Karl Landsteiner (1868–1943) discovers blood types.

NOW JUMP TO... ❯ MOON LANDINGS page 118; ❯ MARS PROBES page 120

THE Sun

dnesday, April 1, 1903   1d

or liar . . Pearse

ddle

ver

ght'

y Kiwi

EXCLUSIVE
LUKE ATMEE

RMER was at
centre of a
ry last night
claims that he
LOWN aboard an
ft he made.

-witnesses say
Zealander Rich-
Pearse, 25, flew
l hundred yards
s tiny powered
yesterday before
ng into a hedge
end of a field.
is thought he
ained a height
bout 10ft in

nded . . . Kiwi bird

Canterbury on
outh Island.

ue, Pearse, a tal-
engineer who
s most of his
poring over sci-
magazines, will
wn in history as
st man to fly.
there is consid-
doubt over his
No one in the
ay land of the
a famously
TLESS bird,
clear photos of
e's alleged feat.
n local newspa-
seem reluctant
port it. A flight
t said: "This
should probably
ck to his sheep."

Vision. . . Tsiolkovsky
and, right, drawing
of proposed rocket

ROCKET MAN

Amazing 'space voyage' plan

A MATHS teacher claims man
could go into space on a
ROCKET — even though we
haven't flown a PLANE yet.

Konstantin Tsiolkovsky, 45,
details how the rockets would
work. And in a book called
The Exploration of Cosmic

By COSMO NORT, Sun Spaceman

Space by Means of Reaction
Devices he suggests we could
build "space stations" and
colonise other planets.

Tsiolkovsky lives in a log
cabin in Kaluga, Russia, is

almost deaf and was taught
at home as a child. He said:
"One day we'll control the
solar system AND the Earth."

One sceptic said: "He's jumping the gun. So far we've only
flown balloons and gliders."

Head In The Clouds — Page 9

1903 THE WRIGHT BROTHERS AND POWERED FLIGHT

AIR travel is so commonplace and so essential to the modern world is it hard to believe the first successful, powered flight came little more than a century ago. Leonardo da Vinci studied the mechanics of flight as early as the 15th century, but it took two bicycle repairmen to achieve it in 1903.

The quest for human flight began in earnest with the hot air balloon, invented and successfully tested by two French brothers, Joseph and Jacques Montgolfier (1740–1810 and 1745–1799), in 1783. That was followed quickly by airships using balloons filled with hydrogen.

Pioneers of winged aircraft tried to mirror the way birds achieve flight – by flapping. A bird generates both power and lift with its wings, but copying that proved impossible. In 1799, English physicist George Cayley (1773–1857) realised the way forward would be to separate the power from the lift. He worked out the basics of aerodynamics: how a wing moving through the air generates a lifting force. All that was needed then was a source of power to push the aeroplane through the air. Cayley drew designs for aeroplanes with all the basic features of modern aircraft.

For most of the 19th century, the steam engine was the only power source available. People tried in vain to

Dynamic man George Cayley, the first person to think scientifically about aerodynamics and how airflow around a wing can produce lift. He is the 'father of fixed wing aircraft'.

French pilot On 25th July 1909, Louis Bleriot (1872-1936) became the first person to fly across the English Channel. Here, his plane has crash-landed in Dover.

Steam carriage Fictitious view of Henson's Aerial Steam Carriage, from 1843. William Henson (1812–1888) patented this machine, but it never flew – the steam engine would have been too heavy.

design a Cayley-style aeroplane with a steam engine connected to a propeller. The problem was that a steam engine with enough power made the plane too heavy. Englishman John Stringfellow (1799–1883) did build a steam-powered flying machine that made a short flight in 1848. But the most successful flights of the 19th century were with unpowered gliders. The most famous glider pilot was German Otto Lilienthal (1848–1896) who flew with great control for long periods, much as a modern hang glider does. Between 1891 and his death in a gliding accident, Lilienthal made more than 2,000 successful flights.

MIND BOGGLER
● The fastest manned jet plane was the U.S. military's Lockheed SR-71, with a top speed of 3,529.56 kph (2,188 mph). However, the U.S. air force and navy's experimental rocket-powered X-15 plane was the fastest manned aircraft ever, hitting 7,274 kph (4,510 mph) in 1967.

The invention of the internal combustion engine, powerful but light, brought the dream of powered flight closer. Several people began working on designs. Two were Ohio brothers Wilbur and Orville Wright (1867–1912 and 1871–1948), skilled engineers who turned their attentions to flight around 1896 after a decade building and fixing bicycles.

They built their own engine and propeller to power a plane based on Lilienthal's gliders. The 'Flyer' was tested in the gusty open spaces of Kill Devil Hills near Kitty Hawk, North Carolina. It had a 12-metre (39ft) wingspan and weighed 340 kg (750lb) including the pilot.

Orville went up first – and his 12-second flight put him in the history books. By 1905, the Wrights improved their plane and were able to fly as long as the fuel lasted.

Progress in flight was rapid in the next 20 years, with the military advantages of aircraft being quickly realised during World War I. The first airlines began carrying passengers across oceans and continents in the 1920s. Aeroplanes played a huge role in World War II, and it was during that war the first jet engines were used. Afterwards, the aviation industry expanded, opening up the world to leisure and business travellers.

Now, just over 100 years since Orville Wright first took to the skies, air passengers take around FOUR BILLION flights a year.

Long haul John Alcock, (1892-1919) and Arthur Whitten Brown (1886-1948) made the first transatlantic flight in 1919 in this Vickers-Vimy aeroplane, seen here leaving St. Johns, Newfoundland, on its way to Clifden, Ireland.

NOW JUMP TO... ◀ LEONARDO DA VINCI page 24; ▶ CONCORDE page 116

THE Sun

Friday, December 18, 1903

1d

RIGHT: Orville went up first . . .

LEFT: Wilbur flew further than brother

STRAIGHTEN UP

AND FLY, WRIGHT

Bike repairers go 852ft in engine-driven plane

OVERJOYED Orville Wright made history yesterday as the first human to fly a powered aircraft.

American Orville, 32, stayed in the air for 12 seconds and covered 120ft in the rickety-looking biplane he built with his brother Wilbur.

Then 36-year-old Wilbur had a go in the propellered

By HEATH ROWE and **STAN STEAD**

plane, which has a 12-horse-power engine. By the end of the day he had gone one better than Orville — staying up

for a full 59 seconds and covering a whopping 852ft at Kill Devil Hills near Kitty Hawk, North Carolina.

Orville's first flight was photographed *(see above)*

and witnessed by five locals. Unfortunately, the aircraft was then wrecked when a gust of wind flipped it over as the men stood around discussing their feat. The

Wrights, who own a bicycle repair shop in Dayton, Ohio, hope to fix it.

They also aim to repeat their flying achievement back in Ohio, without the help of the strong winds which made them choose Kitty Hawk as the best venue for their debut flight.

The Wrights have now boldly gone where no man has gone before — succeeding where dozens of brave and foolhardy folk failed.

Magnificent Men — Pages 4 & 5

THE '10ft HIGH' CLUB

THE Wrights flew at an altitude of about 10ft — and last night dozens of people were hoping to join their

select "club". One couple contacted The Sun last night and said: "This has really fired everyone's imagination.

We can't wait to build a plane and get it up. There is no end of things you could do at 10ft."

FLAP OF HONOUR

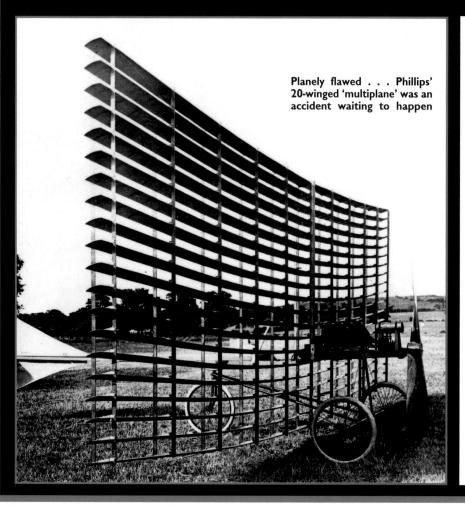

Planely flawed . . . Phillips' 20-winged 'multiplane' was an accident waiting to happen

Flight heroes never got it quite Wright

By AIREY BOURNE, Aviation Correspondent

THE Sun today salutes the magnificent men their flying machines whose heroic efforts pav the way for the Wrights' success.

It all started with Frenchmen Pilâtre de Rozier a François Laurent Marquis d'Arlandes making the fi documented human flight in 1783, in a hot-air ball invented by the Montgolfier brothers.

Then came a century of amazing aviation experiments. Yo shireman George Cayley worked out that an aircraft nee fixed wings, a fuselage and a tail with a rudder. His serv was the guinea pig for the first manned glider flight in 185

Frenchman Jean-Marie Le Bris flew in a wacky gli shaped like an albatross in 1868. And German Otto Lilient made 2,000 glider flights before one killed him in 1896.

The quest for **POWERED** flight had a string of eccen pioneers. John Stringfellow's steam-driven glider is said have achieved a brief unmanned flight in 1848 at Chard, Somerset.

Machine-gun inventor Hiram Ste- vens Maxim *(inset)* achieved takeoff **HIMSELF** in 1894 in a steam-driven "kite", briefly flying at just 3ft.

Cambridgeshire JP Edward Frost was convinced "birdlike" flapping wings were the answer. Just last year he made an "ornithopter" of willow, silk and feathers. It failed.

And Horatio Phillips was on the right lines in 1893 with his petrol- driven craft . . . except his "multi- plane" had 20 wings. It **DID** get off the ground — before collapsing due to inherent structural problems.

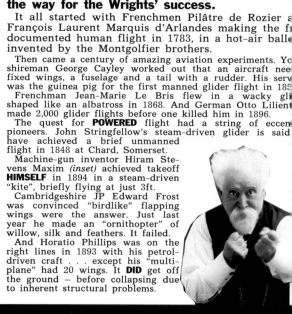

Fatal attraction . . . glider expert Lilienthal

Is it a bird . . . Le Bris's barmy 'albatross' glider

Wing and a prayer . . . Frost's birdlike, flapping orni-thopter was not a big success

Full steam ahead . . . Stringfellow flew powered glider. This is his triplane

Dream on . . . how we'd look if we flew by pulling levers to flap wings

1905 EINSTEIN: BIGGEST 'STAR' OF SCIENCE

MOST people associate Albert Einstein, probably the most famous scientist of all time, with a single equation: E = mc². But Einstein contributed much, much more, perhaps most notably his Special Theory of Relativity, which changed our understanding of the universe.

A German-American physicist, Einstein (1879–1955) wrote four enormously important papers in 1905, often dubbed his 'annus mirabilis' or 'wonderful year'.

The first was a piece of mathematical brilliance that explained 'Brownian motion' – the constant, random movement of tiny pollen grains in water seen under a microscope. It had puzzled scientists since the 1820s. Einstein said it was caused by water molecules bumping into the pollen.

His other three papers were ground-breaking and revolutionary. The first involved a phenomenon called the photoelectric effect, in which light causes electrons to be ejected from the surface of a metal. Before 1905, most scientists believed light is simply a wave motion, a disturbance in electric and magnetic fields. But that could not fully explain the photoelectric effect. Einstein said light is a stream of particles called photons. We now know that both interpretations are correct: light and other forms of electromagnetic radiation behave as both waves and particles. Einstein's explanation won him the Nobel Prize for physics in 1921.

The next paper introduced a radical new idea we now call the Special Theory of Relativity, which transformed scientists' understanding of space and time. Special Relativity gave rise to the idea that there was more to the universe than the familiar three dimensions. Einstein described the universe as a four-dimensional place where

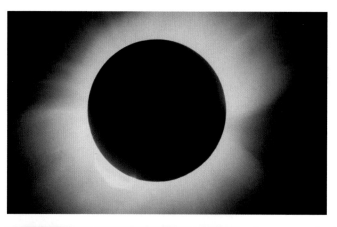

Children's puzzle Einstein, pictured in 1933, solving a puzzle sent to him by a child – Einstein's fame spread to every age group and every nation.

things happen in 'space-time' – rather than a three-dimensional one where time ticks away independently of space. He also said time and space are not fixed, contrary to Isaac Newton's view that they are both absolute.

Einstein's famous mass-energy equation appeared in the last of his 1905 papers. One of the consequences of Special Relativity is that mass and energy are two forms of the same thing, which physicists call mass-energy. Mass (m) can be converted into energy (E), and vice versa. And because the two are related by a huge number – the speed of light squared (c^2), which is 34,596,000,000 – a tiny amount of matter yields a huge amount of energy. A spent fuel rod in a nuclear reactor weighs a fraction of a gram less than a fresh one, even though it has produced enough energy to power thousands of homes for months.

Special Relativity included what scientists

Shadowy evidence Photograph of the 1919 solar eclipse, taken at Sobral in Brazil. Astronomers here and on another expedition off the west coast of Africa found dramatic confirmation of Einstein's General Theory of Relativity.

knew about electric and magnetic forces – but it did not deal with gravity. In 1916, Einstein published his General Theory of Relativity, showing that gravity can be explained as the 'warping' of space-time. He said clocks would run more slowly in intense gravitational fields near very massive objects and that light, normally assumed to travel in perfectly straight lines, would follow the curve of warped space-time.

Photographs taken during a total solar eclipse in 1919 proved that light from distant stars bent as it passed close to the sun – by exactly the amount Einstein's theory predicted. When the news broke it made Einstein an instant worldwide celebrity – very unusual for a scientist. And all the tests of relativity to date have proved Einstein's ideas correct.

Important work This copy of the combined Special and General Theory of Relativity from 1917 was signed by Einstein himself.

MIND BOGGLER

● Inside the sun, mass is converted to energy at the rate of four million tonnes a second by nuclear reactions deep in its core.

WHAT IN THE WORLD?

1903 Dutch physiologist Willem Einthoven (1860–1927) invents an early type of electrocardiograph to record the electrical activity of the heart.

1903 New Zealand-born British physicist Ernest Rutherford (1871–1937) experiments with alpha rays, discovering they are positively charged.

1904 Following earlier aborted attempts, work begins in earnest on the Panama Canal.

1904 JJ Thomson suggests the 'plum pudding' model of the structure of atoms, in which electrons are distributed in a sphere of positive charge.

Ultimate test Einstein's theories of relativity have been tested in many different ways. In 2005–2006, a spacecraft called Gravity Probe B spent a year in orbit around the Earth measuring the warping of space-time caused by the Earth.

NOW JUMP TO... ◐ BIG BANG page 6; ◑ ATOMIC THEORY page 96; ◒ TIME TRAVEL page 136

THE Sun

Friday, November 17, 1905

1d

Mass hysteria

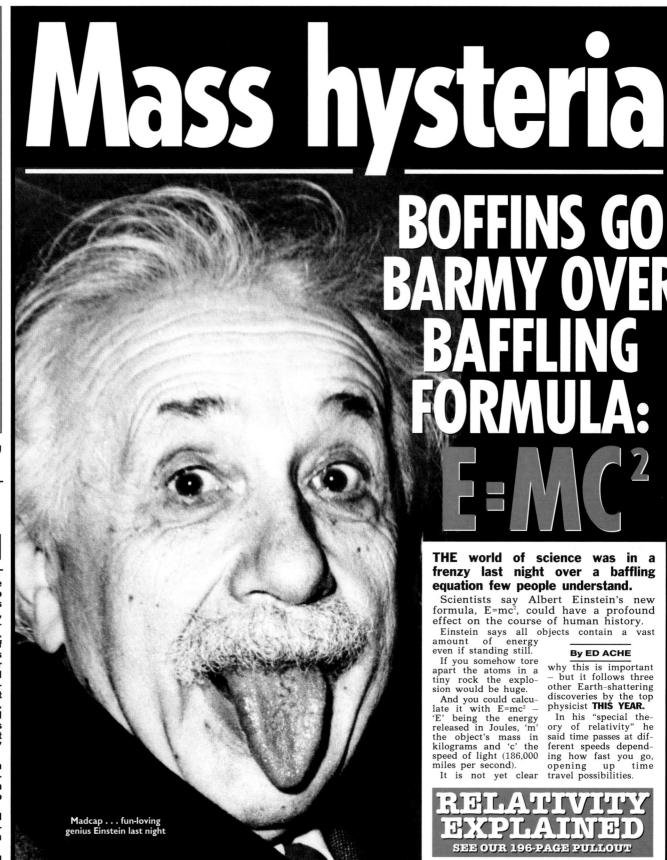

Madcap . . . fun-loving genius Einstein last night

BOFFINS GO BARMY OVER BAFFLING FORMULA: $E = MC^2$

THE world of science was in a frenzy last night over a baffling equation few people understand.

Scientists say Albert Einstein's new formula, $E=mc^2$, could have a profound effect on the course of human history.

Einstein says all objects contain a vast amount of energy even if standing still.

If you somehow tore apart the atoms in a tiny rock the explosion would be huge.

And you could calculate it with $E=mc^2$ – 'E' being the energy released in Joules, 'm' the object's mass in kilograms and 'c' the speed of light (186,000 miles per second).

It is not yet clear

By ED ACHE

why this is important – but it follows three other Earth-shattering discoveries by the top physicist **THIS YEAR**.

In his "special theory of relativity" he said time passes at different speeds depending how fast you go, opening up time travel possibilities.

RELATIVITY EXPLAINED
SEE OUR 196-PAGE PULLOUT

● 89

1911 MARIE CURIE: TOP WOMAN IN SCIENCE

MARIE Curie is the most famous woman scientist of all time and the first person to win two Nobel prizes. She is best remembered for her research into radioactivity, which almost certainly led to her death.

Henri Becquerel (1852–1908) discovered radioactivity in 1896 while trying to find out more about X-rays. Convinced they had something to do with phosphorescent minerals, which glow in the dark after exposure to light, he wrapped various minerals in photographic paper. He found that compounds of uranium affected the photographic paper even when they had not been illuminated.

Curie (1867–1934), a Polish-born French chemist and physicist, showed that this phenomenon, which she dubbed 'radioactivity', was not restricted to uranium compounds. She observed the same thing with the element thorium. With her husband Pierre (1859–1906), she went on to discover two previously unknown radioactive elements. They named one polonium, after Curie's native country, and the other radium, because it is extremely radioactive. Her radioactivity research won her a first Nobel in 1903, jointly with Pierre and Becquerel. (The second, in 1911, was for discovering and studying radium).

Other scientists quickly began to work out more about Becquerel's mysterious rays. They discovered

MIND BOGGLER
● Some equipment from Curie's laboratory, donated to the Science Museum after her death, is held in a special strongroom. After more than fifty years, it is still dangerously radioactive.

Measuring device Ionisation chamber made by Pierre Curie as a way of measuring the intensity of radioactivity. Radiation ionises the gas inside the device, making it conduct electricity. The more intense the radiation, the more the gas conducts.

A man's world Today, science is not at all as male-dominated as it was in Curie's day. This photograph was taken at the first Solvay Physics Conference, in 1911. Curie (seated) was the only woman present. Ernest Rutherford is the tall man directly behind her. Paul Langevin was also there (far right) standing next to Albert Einstein.

there are three different types: alpha, beta and gamma radiation. The first is a stream of positively charged particles called 'alpha particles'; the second a stream of negatively charged 'beta particles'; the third type, gamma radiation, is similar to X-rays – a form of electromagnetic radiation.

Scientists knew early on that X-rays can cause burns, but they only gradually became aware of the harmful effects of radioactivity. Curie herself died of aplastic anaemia – a disease of the blood almost certainly caused by her excessive exposure to radioactivity.

During the 1910s and 1920s, it became clear that radioactivity originates in the atomic nucleus, the concentration of positive charge at the centre of an atom.

The number of positive charges in the nucleus defines what element a particular atom is. The nucleus of a helium atom has twice as many as that of a hydrogen atom; a uranium atom has 92 times as many. The more charges a nucleus has, the bigger it is. And bigger nuclei are unstable, which explains why only some elements – including uranium – are radioactive. When the nuclei of radioactive atoms emit alpha or beta rays, the number of nuclear charges changes – in other words, an atom

Henri Becquerel, discoverer of radioactivity, photographed in his laboratory.

changes into another element. For example, when a uranium atom emits an alpha particle, it becomes a thorium atom.

● In 1910, Curie, by then a widow, is said to have had an affair with the married French physicist Paul Langevin (1872–1946), which scandalised the French public. But Curie later became a darling of the French: she appeared on a banknote, and in 1995 her body was entombed in the Panthéon, a burial place in Paris reserved for VIPs. She is the only woman buried there.

Alpha rays Photograph showing the tracks of alpha rays from polonium in a cloud chamber: a box containing alcohol vapour. The cloud chamber was invented by Scottish physicist Charles Wilson (1869–1959), in 1900.

WHAT IN THE WORLD?

1906 BCG (Bacilli-Calmette-Guerin) immunisation for tuberculosis first developed.

1906 The first modern electric vacuum cleaner is invented by janitor James Spangler.

1906 Canadian inventor Reginald Fessenden (1866–1932) makes the first broadcast of sound on radio, which was heard by ships at sea.

1906 Belgian-American chemist Leo Baekeland (1863–1944) makes the first completely synthetic plastic, Bakelite.

1907 Russian psychologist Ivan Pavlov (1849–1936) carries out his famous research, 'conditioning' dogs to salivate at the sound of a bell.

1907 Lee de Forest (1873–1961) invents the Audion, the first electronic component capable of amplification.

1909 French aviator Louis Blériot (1872–1936) becomes the first person to fly across the English channel.

NOW JUMP TO... ◆ X-RAYS page 78; ◆ ATOMIC FISSION page 102

Pierre . . . killed by horse

Docs: Crazy Curie risking her life

By PHIL HARDY

DOCTORS last night warned that Marie may be risking her life with radium.

The chemical element she and husband Pierre discovered is radioactive.

And although it is not known if radioactivity is harmful, Marie has suffered catalogue of health problems.

Her fingertips are scarred from handling samples and she is said to be in constant pain.

Moth

Pierre had severe back and leg pains before he was killed by a horse and carriage in Paris five years ago.

But Marie is still drawn to her mystery substances like a moth to a flame.

She even keeps a jar of radium salts by her bed because she likes their blue glow in the dark.

One doctor said: "We know so little about these chemicals. They could be the death of her."

Target . . . Marie has won TWO Nobels, but French are hounding her

FLASK TANGO IN PARIS

Sex scandal of Nobel winner
Marie and married scientist

By RAY DIATION

THE world's top woman scientist was targeted by hate mobs last night over a fling with a married man.

Widow Marie Curie, 44, winner of **TWO** Nobel Prizes, is said to have lured physicist Paul Langevin *(right)* away from his wife in Paris.

France's Press and public are up in arms, mainly because she is Polish. Radioactivity pioneer Marie insists her private life is her own business.

You Glow, Girl — Page 7

● 91

1924 AN INSIGHT INTO THE VASTNESS OF SPACE

THE confirmation by astronomer Edwin Hubble that the giant spiral of stars known as Andromeda was a separate galaxy well beyond our own Milky Way shed light for the first time on the unimaginable scale of the universe.

When Galileo Galilei (1564–1642) looked through his telescope at the Milky Way – a broad, fuzzy band stretching across the night sky – he could see it was made of countless distant stars. All of these, plus those close enough to be seen as individual points of light, are in the Milky Way galaxy. We live near the edge; the fuzzy band across the sky is a result of looking towards the centre where there is a greater density of distant stars.

There are also smaller fuzzy patches distributed throughout the sky. Astronomers initially called them 'nebulae' (nebulas) from the Latin word for cloud. Some are visible to the naked eye, but many more can be seen through a telescope. Many are clouds of gas and dust inside our galaxy from which new stars form – but not all.

In 1781, French astronomer Charles Messier (1730–1817) published a catalogue of 103 nebulae. Throughout the next century astronomers wondered what they might be. The most puzzling was Andromeda, also known as 'Messier 31' (M31). It had been observed for hundreds of years – it is just bright enough to see with the naked eye. The first photographs of M31, taken in 1887, revealed it as a spiral.

In 1885, astronomers saw what they thought was a bright 'new star' appear in M31. Stars like this had been seen in our own galaxy – they are called novae (novas), and they are actually old stars flaring up near the ends of their lives. The nova in M31 appeared as bright as those they had seen before, so most astronomers concluded M31 must be part of the Milky Way.

Space telescope In 1990, NASA (the U.S. National Aeronautics and Space Administration) launched the Hubble Space Telescope into Earth orbit. The telescope is named after Edwin Hubble.

But others were convinced M31 was a separate star system outside our galaxy, which would make the nova much further away and especially bright. The puzzle would be solved if someone could work out the size of our galaxy and the distance to M31.

In 1912, American astronomer Henrietta Leavitt (1868–1921) discovered a way of working out distances to one kind of star known as a 'Cepheid variable'. These stars 'pulse', regularly expanding and contracting over periods of a few days to a few weeks. Leavitt discovered a link between the duration of each pulse and a star's inherent brightness. Its distance could then be calculated from the relation between how bright that star appears on Earth and how bright we know it to be from the length of its pulse.

In 1918, another American astronomer, Harlow Shapley (1885-1972), used Leavitt's method to estimate the size of our galaxy – it was larger than anyone had imagined.

Andromeda galaxy (M31), 29 December 1888 One of the earliest photographs of the Andromeda galaxy, then the Andromeda nebula. It was taken by English astronomer Isaac Roberts (1829–1904) in 1888.

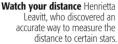

Watch your distance Henrietta Leavitt, who discovered an accurate way to measure the distance to certain stars.

> ## MIND BOGGLER
> ● If the Milky Way was reduced to 80 miles across, our solar system would be 2mm wide on the same scale.

Edwin Hubble (1889–1953), another American, finally settled the Andromeda question. In 1924 he was using what was then the world's largest telescope – at Mount Wilson observatory in California – to examine M31. Hubble saw individual stars in its spiral arms and identified Cepheid variables. He estimated their distance away, and the results showed M31 to be about two million light years away (11,756,964,328,322,000,000 miles), well beyond the limits of our galaxy, and thus proved Andromeda is a huge, separate star system like our own galaxy.

We now know there are hundreds of billions of galaxies in the universe. Each contains billions of stars.

Star birth The Pleiades (M45), a bright cluster of young stars in the constellation of Taurus. The stars are surrounded by gas and dust, which their bluish light illuminates.

WHAT IN THE WORLD?

1911 New Zealander Ernest Rutherford (1871–1937) suggests that each atom's positive charge is concentrated at the centre, in the 'nucleus'.

1912 William Henry Bragg (1862–1942) and his son William Lawrence Bragg (1890–1971) measure the wavelength of X-rays for the first time.

1912 The maiden voyage of the huge ocean liner *Titanic* ends in disaster – 1,500 people perish.

1913 Physicists Charles Fabry (1867–1945) and Henri Buisson (1873–1944) discover the ozone layer.

1913 American industrialist Henry Ford (1863–1947) develops the first true production line, on which cars are made as they pass along a conveyor belt.

1914 The beginning of World War I, which ends in 1918.

1915 Albert Einstein (1879–1955) completes his General Theory of Relativity.

1916 Windscreen wipers are introduced.

1917 The October Revolution, in Russia, overthrows the Russian government, putting the Bolsheviks into power.

1921 Albert Hull (1880–1966) invents the magnetron, a device that produces microwave radiation.

1923 French physicist Louis de Broglie (1892–1987) introduces the idea that all particles also behave as waves and all waves also behave as particles (wave-particle duality).

NOW JUMP TO... ➌ BIG BANG page 6; ➌ GALILEO page 28; ➌ SPACE EXPLORATION page 120 ➌ ALIEN CONTACT page 138

FOUND: A GALAXY FAR, FAR AWAY

Andromeda 'outside Milky Way'

Edwin's star . . . Hubble peers through telescope

OUR Milky Way is NOT the only galaxy in the universe, it was announced last night.

A cluster of stars known as Andromeda has been found to be an enormous galaxy about two million light years from Earth.

By **ANNA KIN** and **BOB AFETTE**

That puts it well outside the boundaries of the Milky Way.

And it opens up astonishing possibilities about the mind-boggling size of the universe — as well as other life it may contain. Andromeda has been known of for centuries and is in fact visible to the naked eye. It was thought to be just another glowing spiral of gas.

But astronomer Edwin Hubble, 35, has now worked out its immense distance away using a 100-inch diameter telescope at Mount Wilson Observatory in California.

He also believes the universe is **EXPANDING.**

Lovely Hubbly — Page Nine

1926 TV, ITS INVENTOR AND ITS FIRST STAR

Mechanical approach Baird's television apparatus from 1926. You can see the subject of Baird's first transmissions, the head of a ventriloquist's dummy called Stookie Bill.

Down the tube The Emitron tube, similar in design to Zworykin's iconoscope, produced a television signal using a scanning electron beam.

TELEVISION is one of the greatest technological advances of the 20th century. It was invented by a Scotsman who funded his initial experiments by working as a shoeshine boy and a razor blade salesman.

Several inventors in the USA and Europe were experimenting with television systems in the early years of the last century. Some worked on all-electronic versions, but Scottish-born John Logie Baird (1888–1946) used a partly mechanical approach.

The main feature of his transmitter was a spinning cardboard disc cut from a hat box. It had holes in it, and inside each was a lens. The holes were arranged in a spiral, and as the disc turned it scanned the scene in front of it. Behind the disc was a light-sensitive detector. German engineer Paul Nipkow (1860–1940) had suggested this set-up long before, in 1884. The picture produced by Baird's 'Televisor' was comprised of 30 lines – just enough detail to make out a human face.

In 1925, he succeeded in transmitting the first picture – of a ventriloquist's dummy named Stookie Bill – from one end of his attic flat in London to the other. He then paid a local office boy to stand in for Stookie – and the teenager became the first person ever shown on TV. On January

Cut away In this 1994 Philips colour television set, you can see the cathode ray tube, with a large flat screen.

MIND BOGGLER

● Such is the impact of Baird's invention that the average Briton now watches TV for the best part of three hours every day. About 41 million TVs are in use in this country alone.

26th 1926 Baird invited scientists and a reporter to the flat and showed them what he had achieved.

Later that year he formed the Baird Television Development Company Ltd. – and the world's first television station, 2TV. In 1927 he sent a live 30-line television signal 730 kilometres (438 miles) from London to Glasgow along telephone cables.

Baird was responsible for several other innovations in television. In 1928, his company sent the first transatlantic signal, from London to New York. He also invented an early colour TV system and a disc-based video recording system called Phonovision.

Baird made the first television programmes for the British Broadcasting Corporation (BBC) in 1929. His broadcast system for the BBC included sound, but never had more than 240 lines – almost the limit of his mechanical system. Electronic systems would eventually win the day. In 1936, the BBC began regular television programming using an electronic system and broadcasting pictures with 405 lines.

The receiver in this system was a cathode ray tube: a glass vessel with the air removed and a phosphorescent coating on the inside surface at the front. A beam of electrons from the back of the tube hits the screen, tracing out the picture line by line, guided by strong electromagnets. Most TV sets today still work on this principle, first suggested in 1897.

The most challenging element of the system was the camera. Russian inventor Vladimir Zworykin (1889–1982) patented the idea for a

TV camera tube called the iconoscope in 1923 and it remained the basis for TV cameras until the invention of digital video cameras in the late 1980s.

Television became common in Britain after World War II. Colour TV was broadcast in the USA in the 1940s but only a tiny proportion of the public had colour sets until the late 1960s. The first regular colour broadcasts in Britain began in 1967. It began to reach a wider audience during the 1970s and videocassette recorders (VCRs) became widespread in the early 1980s.

Today, flat-screen LCD (liquid crystal display) and plasma televisions are increasingly superseding cathode ray tube TVs. Hard disk recorders and DVD (digital versatile disc) recorders are taking over from VCRs. And more and more people are receiving television via digital signals – either in terrestrial broadcasts, through optical fibre cables or via satellite. Some programmes are also available on the Internet.

Face it The earliest recorded television image, from 1925-6, showing a human face. The image was produced on Baird's Televisor and recorded on Phonovision.

WHAT IN THE WORLD?

1924 Labour Party in government for the first time, under Prime Minister James Ramsay MacDonald (1866–1937).

1924 Malcolm Campbell (1885–1948) breaks the land speed record for the first time, achieving 146.16mph (235.22 kph) in his car, *Bluebird*.

1925 A highly-publicised trial in Dayton, Tennessee, convicts schoolteacher John Scopes for teaching evolution.

NOW JUMP TO... ◀ CINEMA page 76; ▶ DIGITAL DEVELOPMENTS page 126

THE Sun

Wednesday, January 27, 1926   2d

Bill: First 'TV' star

THIS is Stookie Bill, the ventriloquist's dummy who became the first star of "TV" yesterday when he was beamed on to the screen. Mr Baird said: "The image of the dummy's head formed itself on the screen with what appeared to me an almost unbelievable clarity.

"I had got it! I could scarcely believe my eyes and felt myself shaking with excitement."

TV Biz Special On Invention Of TV — Page 24

Genius . . . Darwin

ORRY CHAS!

n chumps ver chimps

an edition of The Sun d November 25, 1859, headlined "Monkey er" we may have inadently given the impres- that we believed les Darwin's theory of ution to have been und.

has been drawn to our ntion that our use of words "mad" and my" may have cast t on Mr Darwin's sug- ion that mankind's stors were apes.

s family have also indi- d to us that by superim- ng Mr Darwin's head the body of a monkey may have unwittingly sed him to ridicule.

e now accept Mr Dar- s theory of evolution is st certainly true and ogise posthumously to for any embarrassment ed.

Genius . . . Jenner

ORRY DDIE!

n missed int on jabs

The Sun of July 2, 1796, er a previous Editor, implied that Dr Edward ner's pioneering work innoculation may have misguided.

r front page article, dlined "A Pox On You, tor", suggested that Dr ner was risking a child's for his own ends.

r use of the words l", "demented" and ckpot" may have fur- implied that we ted his mental capac- o carry out the work.

hindsight, our publica- of a remark from an amed source calling for Jenner to be "hanged" regrettable.

e now accept that Dr ner was one of the most ortant figures in the his- of medicine and apolo- to his descendants for misunderstanding.

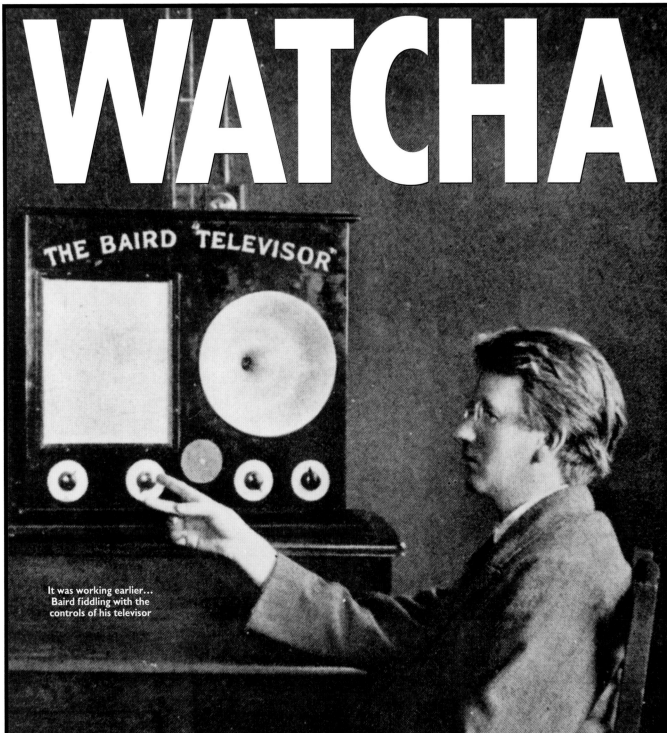

THE BAIRD "TELEVISOR"

It was working earlier... Baird fiddling with the controls of his televisor

WATCHA

'Televisor' beams live pictures on to screen

A MAN has invented a miracle gadget called a "televisor" — out of an old tea chest, some bits of cardboard and string.

It has a small screen which shows live, moving images sent from a camera nearby.

Scottish inventor John Logie Baird, 36, caused amazement when he demonstrated the con-

By DICKY PICTIA

traption yesterday at his flat in London's Soho, after work- ing on it for years. And scien- tists are speculating that one day every home may have a "TV" and receive pictures from all over the world.

Tonight's Telly — Page 43

1927 QUANTUM THEORY & STRUCTURE OF ATOMS

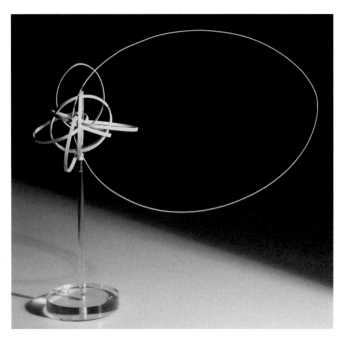

Atomic picture A model of a sodium atom according to the ideas of Niels Bohr. The hoops represent the definite orbits of electrons around a central nucleus (not shown).

GERMAN physicist Werner Heisenberg made great contributions to a vital area of modern physics, quantum theory – most notably with his Uncertainty Principle. Quantum theory describes the world on the smallest scales, at the atomic and subatomic level. It is the most tested theory in physics and the foundation of some of the technology that has transformed the world in the last 50 years.

Quantum mechanics, as it is known, explains the behaviour of the component parts of atoms. They do not conform to the normal laws of physics we experience every day – and, that being so, the theory is often hard for the layman to understand or even believe. Two of the founding fathers of this branch of physics are Heisenberg (1901-1976) and Austrian physicist Erwin Schrödinger (1887–1961).

It all began with an idea from German physicist Max Planck (1858–1947). In 1900, he said that only certain amounts of energy are possible: the 'allowed' energies of a particle, such as an electron, depend upon the situation.

Albert Einstein (1879–1955) used Planck's idea to work out that radiation, such as light, is composed of particles: photons.

In 1913, Danish physicist Niels Bohr (1885–1962) applied Planck's idea to electrons in atoms. At the centre of an atom is a concentration of positive charge, the nucleus. Electrons orbit the nucleus – and the further from it they are, the higher their energy.

If Planck's suggestion was correct, only certain orbits would be possible – nothing in between. Using his idea, Bohr correctly suggested that electrons could jump up a level to a higher orbit if they absorbed energy, and give off energy when they jump back down a level (moving closer to the nucleus). The 'spare' energy would become one of Einstein's photons: as electrons move between orbits, they absorb and emit light. Bohr even worked out what the energy levels should be for the simplest atoms.

Physicists refined and extended Bohr's idea to more complicated atoms, and all was well. But in the 1920s things took a strange turn. Several experiments supported Einstein's idea that electromagnetic radiation, normally thought of as waves, also behaved as particles. Meanwhile

German physicist, and originator of the idea of quantisation, **Max Planck**, about 1910.

Danish physicist **Niels Bohr**, in 1910.

the French physicist Louis de Broglie (1892–1987) suggested the opposite might also be true: particles such as electrons also behave as waves. Several experiments proved his bizarre idea correct.

This 'wave-particle duality' has some strange consequences, since waves behave very differently from particles. Waves, for example, spread out over large areas – how could a particle do that? Electrons – only discovered in 1897 – had always behaved as particles, like solid balls. But experiments showed that they have a 'wavelength' – just like light. Higher-energy electrons have a shorter wavelength than lower-energy electrons.

In 1926, Schrödinger produced a brilliant mathematical equation based on the physics of wave motion to describe the behaviour of tiny particles like electrons. The equation, reportedly arrived at during a Christmas holiday with his mistress in the Alps, works very well and supports the idea of matter behaving as waves.

Physicists interpret the wave nature of particles in terms of probability: the wave describes how likely a particle is to be found in a particular location, and with a particular energy. But one of the strange consequences of quantum theory forms the basis of Heisenberg's Uncertainty Principle – that you cannot know the exact position and velocity of a subatomic particle at the same time.

Quantum theory has done more than give physicists a mathematical window on the reality of tiny systems like atoms. It is routinely applied in many technologies, including lasers and microelectronics, and in making extremely accurate atomic clocks.

Giving a wave Louis de Broglie, pictured in the 1930s.

NOW JUMP TO... ◉ THE CONCEPT OF THE ATOM page 14; ◉ MARIE CURIE page 90

Dear Deidre
I'm in love with a quantum mechanic ...but he's so TINY
No1 AGONY AUNT SORTS IT OUT: PAGE 64

...m-dinger ... Erwin

...omeo
...offin's
...ureka'
...moment
in bed!

...Y CASSIE NOVA

...OOTHIE scientist
...in Schrodinger
produced an
...ation to shake the
...d, while bedding
...lover in the Alps.
...e 39-year-old Aus-
...n left his wife
...nd in London to
...nd last Christmas
...d New Year
...cked up with a
...tress in a chalet.
...is not clear how
...ch time he
...oted to her.

Nutshell

...t by the time he
...e down the moun-
...he had produced
...theory on atoms
...d to be as impor-
...: as Sir Isaac New-
...s laws of motion.
...e equation is far
...indecently com-
...: to publish in a
...ily newspaper.
...a nutshell it pre-
...s the motion of
...tiny particles
...ch make up atoms
...d describes how
...y are affected by
...ernal forces.
...chrodinger's idea
...being dubbed a
...te erotic out-
...st". It is said to
...e launched a new
...nch of physics,
...ntum Mechanics.

D'OH!

Scientist's staggering new theory ..I can't be sure where anything is

BAFFLED? SO'S HE!

By CLAIRE ASMUD

ONE of the world's great scientists has reached a staggeringly frank conclusion: He's not really sure where anything is.

German Werner Heisenberg says that when it comes to electrons you can **NEVER** know where one is or how fast it's going.

He has called this his "Uncertainty Principle" – and is being hailed a genius as a result.

One sceptical rival said: "I'm not always certain where my slippers are, but that's not going to win me the Nobel Prize."

10 Things Werner Doesn't Know— Page 8

● **97**

1928 A GOLDEN AGE OF GREAT INVENTIONS

'Raadvad' hand-operated bread slicer, 1880-1900.

SLICED bread is the classic example of a small idea that made a big difference at a time when people did not have many of the conveniences we enjoy today. It was so revolutionary that it spawned the phrase 'the best thing since sliced bread', to describe any notable innovation thereafter. And it capped a golden period of invention stretching back a century.

Sliced bread was the idea of American inventor Otto Frederick Rohwedder(1880–1960). The first loaves were sold on July 7th 1928 in Chillicothe, Missouri, USA. Rohwedder had the kind of pioneering spirit found in many inventors of his day. Down on his luck, he travelled around with his wife and teenage son, trying to sell his slicing machine. Several bakeries turned him down before he arrived at M.F. Bench's Chillicothe Bakery Company. Frank Bench's grocery store became the first shop anywhere in the world to sell pre-sliced bread and the shop's sales increased by 2,000 per cent in two weeks.

The period 1830-1930, especially from 1880 on, was the heyday for inventors – mainly in the USA – who made themselves busy and rich making life easier or safer. Many visionary people, often from humble backgrounds, made fortunes with simple ideas.

The main driving force behind technological innovation is the patent: the exclusive right to sell or use an invention for a limited period. A patent document holds the details of an invention, the name of the person who invented it and, importantly, the date on which the patent document was filed. The first known patent was awarded in 1421 to the Italian sculptor and architect Filippo Brunelleschi (1377–1446) for his invention of a new type of barge and lifting gear. The patent concept caught on and was adopted across Europe. The U.S. Constitution contains a section concerning patents. The first U.S. patent law was passed in 1790.

Some innovations are one-off ideas that have an immediate impact and become successful very quickly. Before King Camp Gillette (1855–1932) invented the safety razor in 1901, for example, people had to shave with a 'cut-throat' razor – the name is apt. Less than a year after the commercial introduction of the safety razor, Gillette had sold 100,000 handles and more than 12 million blades. Each blade was cheap and carried a small profit for Gillette, but the sheer volume of sales made him a very rich man.

Other important inventions are long-standing ideas that depend on other technologies, such as electric power, before they work reliably. In Britain and the USA, electrification spread quickly in the first 30 years of the 20th century – another reason why the pace of invention was rapid during that period. The washing machine, refrigerator and vacuum cleaner all developed quickly once consumers were receiving a reliable electricity supply.

NOW JUMP TO... ◉ **FLINT TOOLS page 8;** ◉ **ELECTRIC MACHINES page 50**

1927 American aviator Charles Lindbergh (1902–1974) makes the first solo, non-stop flight across the Atlantic.

1927 Belgian Priest and astrophysicist Georges Lemaître (1894–1966) suggests his 'cosmic egg' theory for the beginning of the Universe, later developed and called the Big Bang theory.

1927 The Jazz Singer is the first proper, full-length 'talking picture' (film with sound).

Bread winner Rohwedder, inve of the bread slic machine, picture the 1930s.

Some inventions are deceptively straightforward and may not appear as important or as ingenious today as they were at the time. Sliced bread is a good example: the idea seems simple and obvious now, but in the early 20th century the technology required to hold, slice and package a fresh loaf of bread before it went stale was hard to develop. That's why it took Rohwedder 16 years to perfect.

MIND BOGGLER

● The first fax machine, the Pantelegraph, was invented by an Italian, Giovanni Caselli, in 1865, before the telephone. A transmitter scanned a document with its stylus, sending the results down telegraph wires, where a receiver decoded them and reproduced the contents.

Look sharp Early Gillette safety razor, with its original Bakelite box and some spare blades. This one is from the 1930s.

Hot property A record of the 1769 patent, number 913, awarded to James Watt (1736–1819) for his steam engine with a separate condenser.

A.D. 1769 . . . . . . Nº 913.

SPECIFICATION
OF
JAMES WATT.

STEAM ENGINES, &c.

LONDON:

THE Sun

Monday, July 9, 1928   2d

BEST THING SINCE BREAD

'Pre-sliced' miracle

By ROLAND BUTTER and MARGE REENE

FEAST your eyes on one of the greatest inventions of all time — bread that's **ALREADY SLICED.**

The first sliced loaf went on sale last Friday in Chillicothe, Missouri, U.S.

It is poised to revolutionise, and speed up, the making of sandwiches and toast worldwide.

Inventor Otto Rohwedder, 48, has worked on a slicer for 16 years but has only now found a way to wrap the loaf immediately to keep it fresh.

One food expert said: "Cutting up bread has been a pain for 10,000 years. Otto's brainwave is now the yardstick by which all future inventions must be judged."

Dough Boy — Pages 12 & 13

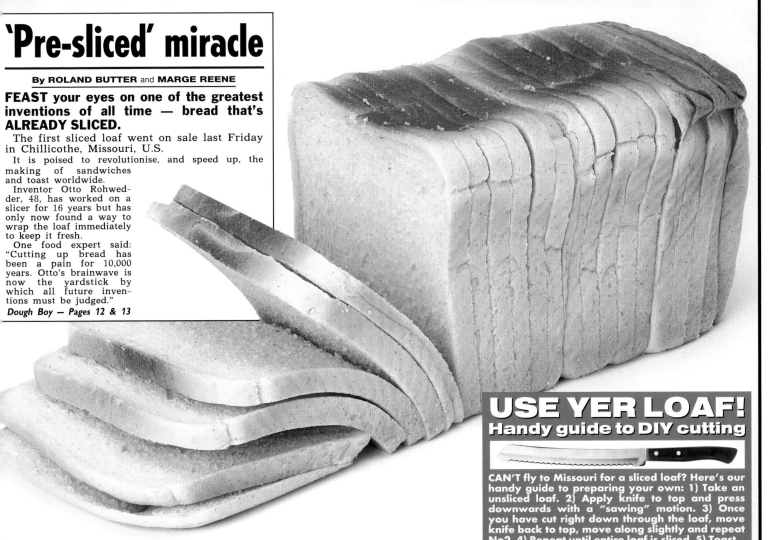

USE YER LOAF!
Handy guide to DIY cutting

CAN'T fly to Missouri for a sliced loaf? Here's our handy guide to preparing your own: 1) Take an unsliced loaf. 2) Apply knife to top and press downwards with a "sawing" motion. 3) Once you have cut right down through the loaf, move knife back to top, move along slightly and repeat No2. 4) Repeat until entire loaf is sliced. 5) Toast.

● **99**

OUT NOW

BRILLIANT NEW SUN MAG

Hot stuff . . . gas cooker

So cool . . . the fridge

Crumbs . . . toaster's pure genius

Soap star . . . the washing machine

Big suck-cess . . . vacuum

Tin-credible . . . cans preserve

A TON OF AMAZING STUFF

After century of great inventions
. . . is sliced bread best of the lot?

By DEE VICE and CON TRAPSHA

THE Sun today salutes a ce
tury of amazing innovatio
— the best things befo
sliced bread.

The last 100 years have se
a golden age of inventio
which have changed our li
beyond recognition.

We all know of the huge bre
throughs — TV, radio, photog
phy, electric light, the pho
flight, cars and passenger trains

*But for many, the little thi
have made the biggest differenc*

Where would we be now wi
out the **FRIDGE,** first built back
1834 by U.S. inventor Jacob P
kins? Now, nearly 100 years la
new "quick-frozen" food inven
by New Yorker Clarence Birds
is about to take off everywhere

TIN CANS, around since
early 1800s, preserve food too
though they didn't take off u
the middle of last century.

Even the **COOKER** hasn't be
around long, with gas stoves p
ented by Briton James Sharp
1826 and electric ones in 1891.

Housework was far hare
before the electric **WASHI
MACHINE,** first produced in 19
And thank heavens for the el
tric **IRON,** invented in 1882 af
years of powering them with ga

Housewives owe a debt to N
York mechanic Walter Hunt, w
invented the **SEWING MACHINE**
1834 and the **SAFETY PIN** in 184

Hats off too to Ohio jani
James Spangler, who in 1
invented an electric **VACU
CLEANER** from a fan, a box and
pillowcase, then sold the patent
a cousin's hubby, one WH Hoov

When the housework's do
there's the lawn. Imagine keep
the grass down with a scythe
which folk did before Glouce
shire engineer Edwin Budd
invented the **MOWER** in 1830.

Afterwards, what better way
relax than with the **CROSSWO
(invented by Liverpudlian puz
maker Arthur Wynne in 19
while dunking a **TEA BAG** (Ame
can Thomas Sullivan in 1908) a
listening to a **GRAMOPHONE** reco
(German Emile Berliner in 1887

Maybe you could even use
TOASTER (invented in 1905) . . .
a piece of the new sliced bread!

Kit!

Launch issue — 6d

144 pages of boys' toys and cutting-edge gizmos for the home

Irons! Something hot for the little lady – new designs warm up in less than an hour

Mobiles! Can be moved ANYWHERE (within a two-foot radius)

News! Chaos as GPO issues 3-digit phone numbers

Hi-fi! Banging bakelite boomboxes

Format wars! Cylinder or disc – which is best?

Mowers! Heavy metal thrashing and slashing

1932 CAMBRIDGE PAIR 'SPLIT THE ATOM'

THE PHRASE 'splitting the atom' is often quoted as a benchmark for scientific discovery. Indeed, the achievement of physicists John Cockcroft and Ernest Walton was monumental, unlocking the secrets of the atomic nucleus, proving Einstein's $E = mc^2$ and opening the door to nuclear power.

The structure of atoms was established by New Zealander Ernest Rutherford in 1911. Each has a positively-charged nucleus surrounded by negatively-charged electrons. The nucleus's positive charge is due to the presence of tiny particles within it called protons. Each chemical element has a unique number of protons in the nucleus of each atom. Every hydrogen nucleus has one, for example; every helium nucleus, two; then lithium, three, beryllium, four, and so on.

Having established that, the next challenge was to delve into the nucleus itself, and try to tear it apart.

Under Rutherford's guidance at the Cavendish Laboratory at Cambridge University, Cockcroft (1897–1967), from England, and Irishman Walton (1903–1995) built the first particle accelerator in 1932.

Ernest Walton (pictured in 1951).

John Cockroft (pictured in the 1940s).

With it they achieved the first artificial 'disintegration' of the nucleus.

Their machine accelerated protons to high speed so they slammed into a target made of the element lithium. Each lithium atom has three protons in its nucleus. Whenever an accelerated proton hit a lithium nucleus, the result was a nucleus with four protons: beryllium. Each newly created beryllium nucleus existed for a fraction of a second, before disintegrating into two fragments (each one a helium nucleus). These nuclear fragments hit a small phosphorescent screen, producing tiny flashes of light – which told Cockcroft and Walton they had succeeded. For hours on end the pair had to lie down with their heads inside a wooden box at the foot of the apparatus, staring at the phosphorescent screen and counting the flashes.

The process of a nucleus splitting in two is called fission, so Cockcroft and Walton's breakthrough was the first example of nuclear fission – although the term is normally reserved for larger nuclei. When some nuclei break apart, the fragments have less mass than the original nucleus. And, as predicted in Einstein's mass-energy equation $E = mc^2$, the 'missing mass' (m) is converted into energy (E).

The device Cockroft and Walton used was a 'linear accelerator' because it moved protons in a straight line. In 1929, American physicist Ernest Lawrence (1901–1958) invented the 'cyclotron', in which particles travel around a (near) circular enclosure, accelerated by electric fields and magnetic pulses. Today most particle accelerators are large, powerful cyclotrons. The biggest is at the Organisation Européenne pour la Recherche Nucléaire (CERN), at their headquarters in Geneva. It is a ring 27 kilometres (16 miles) in diameter.

By accelerating various types of tiny particles to extremely high speeds and colliding them into each other, physicists have been able to test new theories about the smallest constituents of matter, and have discovered a huge family of subatomic particles.

NOW JUMP TO... ◀ MARIE CURIE page 90; ▶ THE ATOMIC BOMB page 106

MIND BOGGLER

● One million million million million (1,000,000,000,000,000,000,000,000) protons would have a mass of less than two grams. About 500,000,000,000 could fit in a full stop.

Nuclear smasher Photograph of Cockroft and Walton's accelerator, taken in 1932 at the Cavendish Laboratory, Cambridge University.

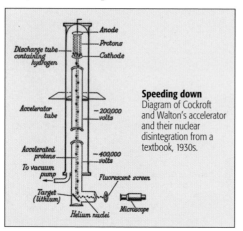

Speeding down Diagram of Cockroft and Walton's accelerator and their nuclear disintegration from a textbook, 1930s.

Anode
Protons
Discharge tube containing hydrogen
Cathode
Accelerator tube
−200,000 volts
Accelerated protons
−400,000 volts
To vacuum pump
Fluorescent screen
Target (lithium)
Microscope
Helium nuclei

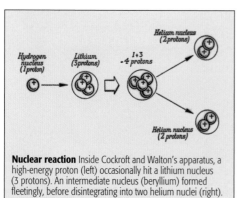

Helium nucleus (2 protons)
Hydrogen nucleus (1 proton)
Lithium (3 protons)
1+3 = 4 protons
Helium nucleus (2 protons)

Nuclear reaction Inside Cockroft and Walton's apparatus, a high-energy proton (left) occasionally hit a lithium nucleus (3 protons). An intermediate nucleus (beryllium) formed fleetingly, before disintegrating into two helium nuclei (right).

Stereo success

The first attempts at recording in stereo were made during the 1930s. The dominant recording technology at the time was vinyl discs, and stereo was made possible by cutting two grooves in the same disc – each following the signal of one of two separate microphones. The earliest surviving stereo recording is from March 1932. Stereo became widely available to the public in the late 1950s.

'Stereophonic' gig

THE first "stereophonic" recording has produced an amazingly lifelike sound, The Sun can reveal. Two microphones were rigged up several feet apart above an orchestra in Philadelphia to simulate what humans hear. The sound from both was "cut" into a wax disc for playback. Full Story: Page 7

NUCLEAR FISHIN'

Sun Angling Editor on reeling in a monster: See Page 94

ATOMIC SPLITTIN'

Brit pair's triumph rocks world's boffins

EXCLUSIVE by ELLIE MENT, Science Correspondent

TWO British scientists have sensationally "split" an atom, winning an international race among boffins.

Cambridge pair John Cockcroft and Ernest Walton used a device they made themselves to tear apart lithium atoms.

Experts reckon the resulting energy release could give mankind a new power source.

Up 'n' Atom — Pages 4 and 5

Little Bang . . . how the 'split' atom might have looked

1940 ANTIBIOTICS: DRUG THAT SAVED MILLIONS

THE era of antibiotics, launched accidentally by the Scottish bacteriologist Alexander Fleming, revolutionised the treatment of humans and animals with bacterial infections. Antibiotics have since saved millions of lives.

An antibiotic is a substance that kills disease-causing, or pathogenic, bacteria without harming a patient. The idea such substances might exist began in the late 19th century when medical researchers identified certain harmless bacteria in soil that could kill pathogenic bacteria. In 1888, German microbiologist E. de Freudenreich managed to isolate an anti-bacterial substance produced by one of these but it was unstable and toxic to humans, ruling it out as a medicine.

The German scientist Paul Ehrlich (1854–1915) took a slightly different approach. He began searching for 'magic bullets': chemicals that would cling to harmful bacteria, but not to human cells. In 1909, he found one – a chemical that could cure syphilis, then a prolific killer. It was 'preparation 606', which he later named 'Salvarsan'.

But penicillin, the first antibiotic, was born one day in 1928 when Fleming (1881–1955) inadvertently let some airborne mould spores

Magic bullets Paul Ehrlich, who founded the science of chemotherapy with his invention of Salvarsan, the first effective cure for syphilis.

WHAT IN THE WORLD?

1934 *Flying Scotsman* becomes the first steam locomotive to travel at more than 100 mph.
1935 Wallace Carothers (1896–1937) develops nylon.
1935 American seismologist Charles Richter (1900–1985) invents a scale for measuring the strength of earthquakes.
1936 The BBC begins regular television programming.
1937 Anglo-German biochemist Hans Krebs (1900–1981) discovers a set of important chemical reactions within living cells, the Krebs Cycle.
1937 '999' becomes Britain's emergency number.
1939 Nazi Germany invades Poland, leading to World War II.

Mould man Alexander Fleming, pictured in 1945.

land on one of his bacterial 'cultures' (colonies grown for research, normally in Petri dishes). The mould, a fungus called penicillium, thrived in the dish. Fleming later realised his mistake – but noticed there were no bacteria around the mould. It was clear that the fungus was producing an antibacterial chemical, which he named penicillin.

For years, Fleming's observation had little impact because no one could isolate the active chemical produced by penicillium. But in 1940, Oxford scientists Howard Florey (1898–1968) and Ernst Chain (1906–1979), along with colleague Norman Heatley (1911–2004), succeeded in isolating small quantities. In 1941, Florey and Heatley went to the USA and helped develop a way of mass-producing penicillin cheaply. The new medicine had an enormous and immediate impact, saving lives throughout World War II. Fleming, Florey and Chain jointly received the Nobel Prize for Medicine in 1945.

Meanwhile, another researcher, French-born bacteriologist René Dubos (1901–1982), isolated an antibacterial chemical produced by soil bacteria. Like Freudenreich's discovery, Dubos' chemical was toxic – but more effective. It could be used on the skin, just not taken internally. Penicillin's effectiveness, and Dubos' work, encouraged other researchers to search for new substances. Concentrating on

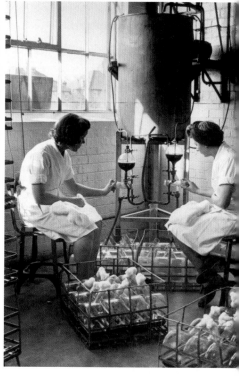

War effort Filling culture flasks with the nutrient solution in which penicillin mould was grown, 1943.

the products of organisms in soil led to the discovery of antibiotics with familiar names such as streptomycin and tetracycline.

Despite the tremendous success of antibiotics, there are problems. A long or concentrated course can kill beneficial bacteria inside your intestines. But more worrying is that bacteria evolve quickly and fresh strains develop that are resistant to certain antibiotics. New versions of an antibiotic can be produced, but the bacteria gradually evolve so that resistant strains become widespread. The most infamous of these is methicillin-resistant staphylococcus aureus (MRSA), known as the 'hospital super-bug'.

MIND BOGGLER
● Inside the human colon is more than a kilogram of beneficial bacteria called 'gut flora', which provide ten per cent of the body's energy by breaking down dietary fibre.

Igor Sikorsky

Russian engineer Igor Sikorsky (1889–1972) had worked on helicopter designs around 1910 and again in the 1920s. When he returned to the problem of 'vertical flight' in the 1930s, he designed the VS-300, which had its first untethered flight in May 1940. This aircraft was a milestone, possessing all the features of most modern helicopters – including a main multi-blade rotor and a tail rotor for stability. At first the VS-300 was controllable in any direction except straight ahead, a problem Sikorsky corrected within a year.

NOW JUMP TO... ◑ JENNER page 46; ◑ PASTEUR page 66; ◑ SANITATION page 72

A GIANT LEAP BACK

A REVOLUTIONARY new single-rotor helicopter has had its maiden flight — but it can't yet go FORWARDS. Russian inventor Igor Sikorsky, 51, made his Vought-Sikorsky 300 go up, down, sideways and backwards. He hopes to go forward next year, saying it is "a minor detail we have not yet solved".

Blade runner . . . Sikorsky

Death Trap — Page 7

Dishing it out . . . Fleming's plucky fungus KOs bugs

MOULD THE FRONT PAGE

Miracle of disease-busting fungus

A CHEMICAL given off by MOULD is a miracle life-saver, The Sun can reveal.

Oxford University boffins Howard Florey and Ernst

By PETE REEDISH, Biology Editor

Chain have already used "penicillin" to save several mice.

They believe it will beat any human bacterial disease, from sore throats to syphilis. Scot Alexander

Fleming discovered penicillin in 1928 when he saw mould in a dish protect itself against bacteria. Florey, 41, and Chain, 34, have figured out how to manufacture it. Florey said: "It looks like a miracle."

Fun Guys — Page 11

FREE INSIDE
Fantastic new 'culture' section

● 105

1945 NUCLEAR POWER IN WAR AND PEACE

THE ATOMIC bombs dropped on Hiroshima and Nagasaki in Japan on August 6th and 9th 1945 are credited with forcing the Japanese to surrender, ending World War II. They are the most dramatic and horrifying displays of nuclear fission the world has seen.

Fat Man Replica of *Fat Man*, the fission bomb dropped on Nagasaki in August 1945. *Fat Man* used plutonium-239 as the fissile material. The bomb dropped on Hiroshima, *Little Boy*, used uranium-235.

WHAT IN THE WORLD?

1940 17,000-year-old cave paintings discovered at Lascaux, France.

1941 The Japanese attack U.S. forces at Pearl Harbour, Hawaii.

1941 Astronomers discover that the outer atmosphere of the sun, the corona, has a temperature of about 1,000,000°C.

1942 The Beveridge Report proposes the Welfare State in Britain.

1944 The Germans use the V-1, and later the same year, the V-2 rocket weapons.

The two weapons detonated with a force equivalent to 15,000 and 21,000 tonnes of conventional explosives. This was made possible by nuclear fission, in which atomic nuclei split in two and release energy. Tens of thousands of people were killed immediately or within hours. Many more have died since from the radioactivity the weapons left behind.

But nuclear fission is not only used in destructive weapons. In peacetime, it is used in research, and to generate electricity in nuclear power stations.

Nuclear fission was first studied in the 1930s when several scientists bombarded heavy elements with particles called neutrons. Some were absorbed into the atomic nuclei, causing the nuclei to become unstable and split into two nearly equal halves. Austrian physicist Lise Meitner (1878–1968) coined the term 'fission' and proved that the process resulted in two elements with smaller nuclei.

Neutrons, normally found with protons in the atomic nucleus, were discovered in 1932

Initial reaction Watercolour record of the world's first nuclear reactor, Chicago Pile No, 1 (1942). It was constructed from graphite blocks containing lumps of uranium, housed in a wooden frame.

by English physicist James Chadwick (1891–1974). While the number of protons in a nucleus defines which element the atom belongs to, the number of neutrons can differ among atoms of the same element. For example, all uranium atoms have 92 protons in their nuclei – but there are several versions, or isotopes, with differing numbers of neutrons.

The classic example of fission involves the isotope uranium-235, whose nuclei have 92 protons and 143 neutrons (92 + 143 = 235). When an individual neutron hits a uranium-235 nucleus, it forms uranium-236, which is very unstable. The new nucleus breaks apart and releases 'spare' neutrons as well as energy (as a burst of gamma rays).

Some of the spare neutrons released during fission may go on to hit other nuclei, in which case the process may repeat – a 'chain reaction'. In a nuclear reactor inside a power station, the reaction is controlled; in a fission bomb it releases large amounts of energy very fast. Some applications of fission use other isotopes, notably plutonium-239.

The first sustained chain reaction occurred in a 'nuclear pile' in a squash court at the University of Chicago in 1942, as part of the U.S. government's Manhattan Project. Led by J Robert Oppenheimer (1904-1967), this was the top-secret mission

Melted earth This rice bowl was recovered from Hiroshima after the explosion of the world's first nuclear weapon. Heat generated by the bomb caused soil to fuse to the bowl.

MIND BOGGLER

● The Manhattan Project, the research and development programme behind America's nuclear weapons during World War II, began on a small scale in 1942 with a miniscule budget of $6,000. By 1945 it employed 130,000 people at a total cost of $2 billion.

that eventually developed the bombs used in 1945. No nuclear weapons have been used in war since 1945, although thousands of warheads exist with a much greater destructive capacity, and there have been more than 2,000 underground or underwater test explosions in peacetime.

The world's first nuclear power station to supply the public was Calder Hall, in Cumbria (now Sellafield), which opened in 1956. Today, about one-fifth of the world's electrical power is generated by nuclear fission. It is clean and convenient, and costs about the same per unit of energy as other forms. However, nuclear power comes with a risk of accidents – such as the one at Chernobyl, Russia, in 1986. Such disasters are extremely rare, but when they happen, radioactive material leaks into the environment. The other problem is the 'spent' rods of fuel which are highly radioactive and have to be encased in concrete, then buried. They gradually become less radioactive, but only over a very long time.

Fuel rods There are several types of nuclear reactor. These uranium fuel rods, coated with magnesium oxide, come from a 'magnox' reactor.

NOW JUMP TO... ● MARIE CURIE page 90; **●** NUCLEAR FISSION page 102

THE Sun

Friday, August 10, 1945   2d

IS THIS THE END?

A mushroom cloud billows over Nagasaki yesterday after America dropped its second atomic bomb on Japan. About 22,000 people died instantly or within hours. Last night the question being asked was: Is it enough to convince Japan that surrender is its only option?

1946 PLASTICS: RISE OF A VAST NEW INDUSTRY

PLASTICS are everywhere today. They are used to make a huge variety of products in our homes, offices and sometimes even inside our bodies. Millions of tonnes of them are thrown away each year. But before 1856, they did not exist at all.

Nylon, used to make stockings, is a synthetic material, which means it does not exist in nature. The first of these ever made was Parkesine, a plastic developed by Alexander Parkes (1813–1890) in 1856. It was made by treating wood fibres with nitric acid.

Soon after came celluloid, patented in 1870 by American printer John Hyatt (1837–1920), who made it as an alternative to ivory for billiard balls. Its most important use since has been as photographic film. In 1909, Leo Baekeland (1863–1944) made Bakelite, a good

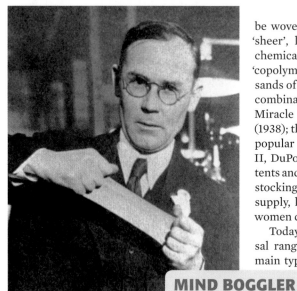

Wallace Carothers, inventor of nylon.

electrical insulator moulded to make electrical appliances such as telephones and radios.

Nylon, Parkesine and celluloid are thermoplastics – they soften when heated and solidify when they cool. But Bakelite is a thermoset: once moulded it 'sets' and will not soften again. Plastics are polymers – they are made of very large molecules formed from lots of small ones joined together. For example, polythene is made from small molecules of a compound called ethylene, obtained from crude oil. Most modern plastics are made from compounds that come from oil or natural gas.

In the quest to find new and better synthetic materials, chemists have strived to understand the process of polymerisation. Several important materials were made early on – but often in quantities that were too small, in forms that were unusable or without their inventors realising what they had done. Polyvinyl chloride (PVC) was first made in the laboratory in 1872 but did not become a useful product until the 1940s. Usually referred to as 'vinyl', it became the standard material for making gramophone records.

Nylon was developed by Wallace Carothers (1896–1937), who joined U.S. manufacturing giant DuPont in 1928. It can be made into fine fibres, which can be woven or knitted into a fabric that is very 'sheer', like silk. It is made by mixing two chemicals, whose molecules join to form a 'copolymer'. Carothers and his team tried thousands of variations before hitting on a winning combination. Their first product was the Miracle Tuft toothbrush with nylon bristles (1938); their stockings went on sale in 1939 as a popular alternative to silk. During World War II, DuPont had to make nylon for parachutes, tents and ropes. Afterwards, it resumed making stockings, but demand seriously outstripped supply, leading to occasional violence among women clamouring for them.

Today, the plastics industry makes a colossal range of materials. There are about fifty main types of plastics and hundreds of different varieties of each type. There is also a new class of plastics called ecoplastics, made from crops such as corn and sugar. Materials scientists are working, albeit so far with limited success, on biodegradable plastics that will not remain in landfill sites for thousands of years.

MIND BOGGLER

● Teflon, now used in non-stick pans, is often said to have been made for the U.S. space programme. This is an urban myth. It was actually discovered by accident by a chemist working for DuPont (of nylon stockings fame) in 1938 . . . while he was trying to make something else.

Trying it on Woman trying on a new pair of nylon stockings she had just bought, after being first in the queue outside a shop in Washington, DC, in October 1945.

Vinyl disc Long playing record from the 1950s, made with a vinyl polymer introduced in 1946.

Ball joint This section of a replacement hip is made from stainless steel and ultra-high molecular weight polythene.

Radiocarbon dating

American chemist Willard Libby (1908–1980) invented a technique known as radiocarbon dating, which can accurately date fossils and archaeological specimens up to about 50,000 years old.

Radiocarbon, or carbon-14, is a radioactive isotope of carbon present in living organisms. When they die it decays at a fixed rate – so the fewer carbon-14 atoms left in a sample, the older it is. Archaeologists measure the radioactivity of the sample: an older one will be less radioactive than a younger one.

WHAT IN THE WORLD?

1945	Germany surrenders to the Allies (7th May), ending the war in Europe.
1945	The first use of the term 'jet stream' to describe fast winds at high altitude.
1945	American team of scientists discovers element number 61, which they name promethium – it fills the last gap in the periodic table below uranium.

NOW JUMP TO... ◄ SMELTING page 12; ► DNA page 112; ► GLOBAL WARMING page 132

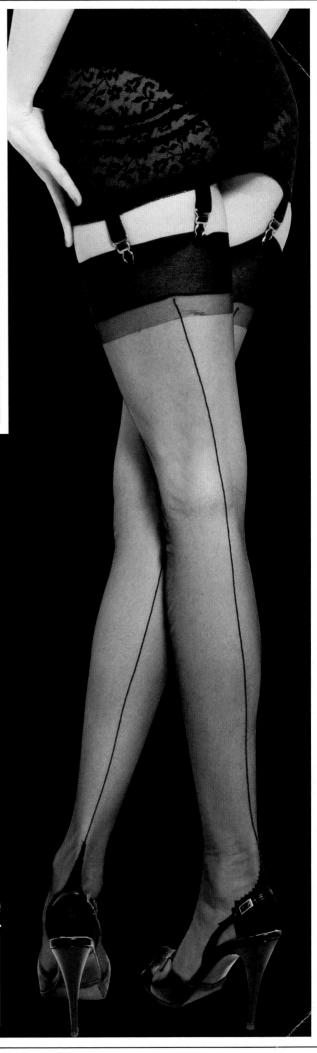

THE Sun

turday, March 23, 1946   2d

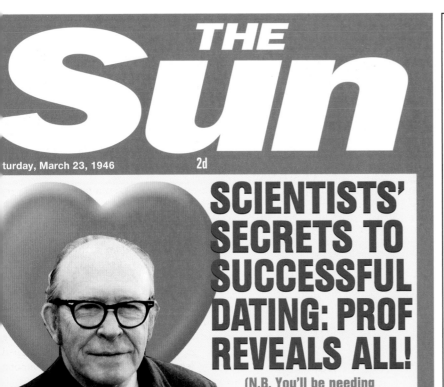

SCIENTISTS' SECRETS TO SUCCESSFUL DATING: PROF REVEALS ALL!

(N.B. You'll be needing the isotope Carbon -14)

A SUN WOMAN SPECIAL INSIDE

THIGH PREDICT A RIOT!

Women brawl over stocking shortage

WOMEN were rioting in the streets last night over a shortage of nylon **STOCKINGS**.

Violence erupted in Pittsburgh, U.S., after 40,000 queued for just 13,000 available pairs. And there are fears

By **PHIL YAFACIN,** Public Disorder Correspondent

similar brawls could hit Britain too.

Trouble flared when manufacturers Du Pont switched from parachutes to stockings *(right)* as the war ended. It could not cope with the demand its ads generated.

So Unseamly — Pages 4 & 5

● 109

1949 THE EVOLUTION OF MODERN COMPUTERS

THE modern world is impossible to imagine without computers. They fit on desks, in laps – even in the palm of the hand. But the first modern computers, one of the earliest being Cambridge University's EDSAC, were very different.

Four elements define a modern computer: a program (a set of instructions); a central processing unit (CPU); a system of input and output; and a memory. The memory stores the program, the input and the results of calculations.

EDSAC (Electronic Delay Storage Automatic Calculator), built by a team led by Maurice Wilkes (b. 1913), was the first practical stored program electronic computer. It ran its first programs on 6th May, 1949, calculating a table of squares and a list of prime numbers.

Its input was via punched paper tape. The memory was a huge array of tubes filled with mercury (called a delay line). The CPU was a system of thermionic valves and output was via a teleprinter.

During the 1950s, computers became slightly smaller – but they were still 'mainframes', found only in large companies and universities. Hardware developed fast and by the end of the decade computers had monitors and keyboards, though punched cards were still common methods of input and output until the 1970s. In 1956, IBM (International Business Machines) introduced magnetic disk memory – the hard disk. The first were housed in cabinets 1.5 metres (5 feet) high, could store about 5 megabytes of data, and cost $500,000.

Cracking codes Two employees of the Women's Royal Naval Service operating Colossus, a World War II programmable computer that deciphered coded German military messages.

MIND BOGGLER

● Home PCs are as much as four million times as fast as EDSAC. EDSAC could carry out 0.00255 million instructions per second. A PC with an Intel Pentium 4 processor can do up to 10,000 million.

The first all-electronic computers used vacuum tubes, electronic components that control electricity flow through the computer's circuits. They were at the heart of how the computers carried out arithmetic. In 1947, an alternative was invented: the transistor, made with semiconductors, such as silicon. It was smaller, faster and more reliable than vacuum tubes and needed less power. In the 1960s, American engineer Jack Kilby (1923–2005) realised that more than one transistor can be placed on a single piece of silicon. This is the basis of the integrated circuit (or 'silicon chip').

Manufacturers in the early 1970s miniaturised the electronic components on their integrated circuits to fit the entire CPU on one chip. American company Intel made the first commercial 'microprocessor' in 1971. This led to smaller, cheaper computers – and rapidly to home computers. The first was the Xerox Alto (1973). It used a 'graphical user interface' (GUI) – graphic icons rather than just words on a

First video game

In 1952, research student AS Douglas wrote a simple noughts and crosses game, called OXO, which ran on EDSAC. It is probably the first computer or video game. The player entered their move using a telephone dial and the game grid was displayed on a tiny screen.

WHAT IN THE WORLD?

1946 First meeting of the United Nations.
1947 Hungarian-British physicist Dennis Gabor (1900–1979) develops the concept of holography (although lasers will not be invented until 1960).
1947 The first commercial microwave oven goes on sale (the first domestic models were sold in 1952).
1947 American test pilot Chuck Yeager (b. 1923) breaks the sound barrier (about 760 mph).
1948 The atomic clock is introduced.
1948 Swiss engineer Georges de Mestral (1907–1990) invents Velcro.

monitor – and was controlled by a mouse. The MITS Altair 8800 followed in 1975 and was the springboard for Bill Gates to launch U.S. software giant Microsoft, which made him the world's richest man.

The popularity of personal computing rose dramatically during the 1980s. There were several popular models – including, in Britain, the Sinclair Spectrum and Acorn's BBC Microcomputer. The machine that made the biggest impact was the IBM-PC (1981). This ran using an operating system written by Microsoft called MS-DOS (Microsoft Disk Operating System). An operating system is a program that manages the computer's hardware and runs the 'application' software.

In 1985, Microsoft introduced a GUI-based system called Windows. Another American company, Apple, had introduced a GUI-based personal computer in 1983. These two systems – now much more sophisticated – still dominate the PC market.

Nowadays many billions of computers vastly more powerful than EDSAC are in use worldwide. Aside from business and personal computers, small 'embedded' computers control a huge range of machines from airlines to digital cameras.

Small computer This Elliot 803 computer (left) from 1963, is smaller than many of its forebears because it was an all-transistor model. This was one of the most successful British computers of the 1960s

Smaller computer The DEC PDP-8 computer (right), the first minicomputer (1965), with the case opened. Input and output were effected via punched paper tape, the switches on the front, or a connected teletype printer.

No mouse The IBM-PC, introduced in 1981. More than 200,000 of these machines were sold in the first year. It had no mouse, because the monitor could only display letters – no graphics.

NOW JUMP TO... ◀ BABBAGE page 52; ▶ DIGITAL DEVELOPMENTS page 126; ▶ THE INTERNET page 128

Geeks' glee over machine's game

STUDENTS at Cambridge are giddy with excitement — after it was revealed EDSAC may be able to play GAMES.

One boffin at the university plans to teach it to play noughts and crosses. Our picture on the left shows how it might look. One student said: "I can't see me getting my thesis written at this rate!"

UNVEILED

The first computer...and it fits in ONE room!

THIS amazing contraption is the world's first practical computer — and it fits in just ONE room.

It uses an incredible array of 3,000 vacuum valves and

By MIKE ROWE-PROCESSOR

tubes filled with mercury. Called "EDSAC" (Electronic Delay Storage Automatic Calculator), it has already produced a table of squares and a list of prime numbers. The Cambridge

University machine, built by top scientist Maurice Wilkes *(pictured left)*, receives its commands from paper tape which is fed into it. It churns out results on a teleprinter.

Unlike previous computers, it can run a variety of "programs".

More dramatic pictures — Centre Pages

1953 THE SHAPE OF DNA & STUDY OF GENETICS

DNA contains the genetic information needed to build life. The discovery of its molecular structure by Francis Crick and James Watson is one of the greatest breakthroughs in the history of biology. At last, biologists could understand how physical characteristics are passed from generation to generation.

In 1857, almost a century before Crick and Watson's discovery, an Austrian monk and botanist, Gregor Mendel (1822–1884), began a remarkable experiment. He carefully bred pea plants with different characteristics – such as the colour or shape of the seeds – and followed how these traits passed through several generations. Mendel worked out that his plants were receiving pairs of 'units of inheritance' – one from each parent – and determined the principles by which that works.

Mendel's results were published in his local natural history society's magazine, instead of an international journal, so they were not widely known. They only came to the attention of international scientists around 1900 when other researchers were making similar discoveries. Mendel's units of inheritance were named 'genes' and the science of heredity became known as 'genetics'.

One of the early pioneers was American zoologist Thomas Hunt Morgan (1866–1945). In 1907 he realised that certain characteristics

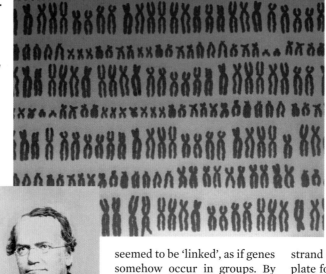

Human chromosomes Different species have different numbers of chromosomes – humans have 23 pairs. The human chromosomes shown here have been arranged in a repeating pattern.

Peas in our time Gregor Mendel, who worked out the laws of genetics in the 1860s.

seemed to be 'linked', as if genes somehow occur in groups. By 1911 he was able to show that genes are carried on chromosomes – long thin structures that could be seen inside cells (in humans there are 46 per cell). Chromosomes had first been observed in 1878, but no one had seen their significance.

Chromosomes are made of two types of compound: proteins and nucleic acids. At first, scientists guessed it must be the proteins that carry genes. But each chromosome also carries a strand of DNA (deoxyribonucleic acid), divided into regions, which are Mendel's units of inheritance: genes. In 1944, Canadian bacteriologist Oswald Avery (1877–1955) showed that DNA could pass on inherited characteristics without any protein present. So scientists turned their attention to the structure of the DNA molecule.

In 1951 American chemist Linus Pauling (1901–1994) worked out the structures of other long biological molecules and found them twisted like a corkscrew – a shape called a helix. He began working on DNA. Meanwhile, at Cambridge University, biologists Crick (1916–2004), an Englishman, and Watson (b. 1928), an American, thought that DNA could be a helical molecule too. But the exact structure they proposed did not agree with the results of experiments by New Zealand biophysicist Maurice Wilkins (b. 1916) and English chemist Rosalind Franklin (1920–1958).

Wilkins and Franklin had been studying DNA at King's College, London, using a technique called X-ray diffraction. Bouncing X-rays off a material produces dots on photographic paper, the pattern of which depends on the arrangement of atoms inside the material. Using Wilkins and Franklin's results, Watson and Crick worked out that certain elements of DNA, called bases, seemed to join up in pairs; DNA had to be a double helix.

They further showed that each strand of DNA in this double helix was a template for the other. That meant that DNA was capable of 'copying' itself without altering its structure.

Rosalind Franklin

Many believe Franklin's role in Watson and Crick's discovery was unfairly played down. Franklin certainly provided key information, and there is controversy over how Wilkins showed Watson her results. In 1962, Crick, Watson and Wilkins won the Nobel Prize for the discovery – Franklin did not. But she had already died of cancer and Nobel Prizes cannot be awarded posthumously.

> ## MIND BOGGLER
> ● DNA was extracted from the tooth of Cheddar man, a 9,000-year-old skeleton found in a Somerset cave. Scientists DNA-tested a few locals – and history teacher Adrian Targett proved to be a descendant.

DNA Model To develop and test their ideas, Crick and Watson made a model of DNA, using these templates to represent groups of atoms. They were able to see that a double helix really works.

WHAT IN THE WORLD?

1949 The North Atlantic Treaty Organisation (NATO) is formed.

1949 Radio waves are detected from the Crab Nebula (M1), which contains a supernova remnant later identified as the first known pulsar.

1949 Egyptian-born English chemist Dorothy Hodgkin (1910–1994) becomes the first person to use an electronic computer to work out a molecular structure (penicillin).

1950 The beginning of the Korean War, as North Korean troops invade South Korea.

1951 Dutch astronomer Jan Oort (1900–1992) produces a detailed map of our galaxy by studying radio waves produced by interstellar hydrogen.

1952 The first nuclear accident, in Canada, where the reactor core explodes.

1952 The world's first sex-change operation is performed.

NOW JUMP TO... ◀ DARWIN page 64; ◀ PLASTICS page 108; ▶ ORIGINS OF LIFE page 114

THE Sun

LOOK A SENSATION IN HAND-ME-DOWN GENES

SUN FASHION SPECIAL — Pages 54-55

onday, April 27, 1953   2d

STRUCTURE OF LIFE

Cambridge pair unveil DNA shape

THIS astonishing image is the DNA molecule which contains the genetic "code" to build life.

It was unveiled by two Cambridge University boffins at the weekend — and is one of the most important scientific finds this century.

Francis Crick and James Watson's announcement of

By POLLY MER

DNA being a "double helix" confirms earlier theories that it contains all the information needed to create most life forms, from a human to a virus. This "code" is also passed on from parents to children — determining anything from hair or eye colour to their vulnerability to disease. The DNA, deoxyribose nucleic acid, is arranged

like a spiral staircase, made up of two intertwined strands of chemical "building blocks", held together by links of hydrogen.

The announcement is a triumph for Briton Crick, 36, *(right)* and American Watson, 25 *(left)*. They were racing top U.S. scientist Linus Pauling to the discovery. The pair had built a model of what they thought DNA **MUST** look like. It was then confirmed by X-ray analysis.

Pure Gene-ius — Page 6

Franklin, my dear... we don't give a damn

THE breakthrough was rocked by controversy yesterday amid claims Crick and Watson "stole" ideas from a woman scientist.

Rosalind Franklin, 32, had been analysing DNA using X-ray techniques at London University while the Cambridge pair were trying to build a model of it from

By NICK IDEAS

metal rods and balls. They knew it was a double helix but had no idea of its dimensions until they saw her unpublished research . . . without her permission.

Critics say she should be given an equal credit for their results, which she

might have arrived at on her own given enough time.

Crick and Watson claim Rosalind freely revealed her findings at a talk she gave.

But one university insider said: "This is just typical of the current dismissive and patronising attitude towards women scientists."

Ten Boffin Babes — Page 3

'Robbed' . . . Franklin

● 113

1953 AMAZING EXPERIMENT GIVES A CLUE TO LIFE

LIFE on Earth is said to have formed somehow from the 'primordial soup' that existed on the early planet. In 1953, the same year scientists discovered the structure of DNA, a student and his professor simulated those conditions – and made the building blocks of life in a flask full of chemicals.

Charles Darwin's theory of evolution showed that all living things are related by common ancestors. Look back far enough, and you reach the beginning of that long process. The oldest fossils show that early life forms were extremely primitive. It seems reasonable to suggest they arose somehow from lifeless matter – a kind of 'chemical evolution'.

In the 1920s, Russian biochemist Aleksandr Oparin (1894–1980) and British biologist J.B.S. Haldane (1892–1964) independently proposed that the complex organic chemicals necessary for life were manufactured in the atmosphere and that rain washed them into the seas, where they formed a 'soup' from which life developed.

The experiment conducted by Stanley Miller (b. 1930) and Harold Urey (1893–1981) at Chicago University involved a loop of glass tubes containing the gases that Oparin and Haldane supposed were in the early Earth's atmosphere. They were connected to a flask full of water and a reaction vessel. Two metal electrodes poked into the reaction vessel and sparks jumped across the gap between them to simulate lightning. The water was heated, so that it evaporated – that way it 'rained'.

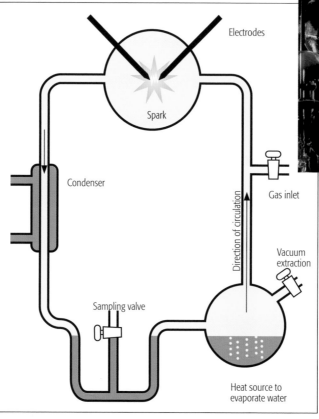

Life drawing This artwork shows the layout of the Miller-Urey experiment. The whole system was sealed from the air, and water circulated around the apparatus thanks to the heat, which made it evaporate.

Electrodes

Spark

Condenser

Gas inlet

Direction of circulation

Vacuum extraction

Sampling valve

Heat source to evaporate water

Stanley Miller, pictured next to a replica of his famous experiment, in the 1990s.

Harold Urey, photographed in the 1950s.

After a week, the two scientists found good quantities of compounds called amino acids inside their apparatus. Amino acids join together to make proteins, complex compounds important to all life on Earth. Miller and Urey's experiment made 13 of the 21 amino acids 'essential' to life as we know it. It was a long way from creating living things or even a complete set of the 'building blocks' of life, but the experiment did show how it is possible to produce a cocktail of complex organic compounds from simple inorganic ingredients.

Since the 1950s, several other scientists have carried out similar experiments with similar results. Other researchers have taken different directions. For example, using radio telescopes, astronomers have discovered complex organic molecules on comets in our solar system and even in huge clouds of gas and dust between the stars.

Many of these interstellar gas clouds contain rich mixtures of chemical elements and receive energy as ultraviolet radiation from nearby stars. They could be 'breeding grounds' for chemical evolution to take place. Our solar system formed from an interstellar cloud; so the ingredients that kicked off evolution on Earth may have formed even before the planet did.

Another promising theory to explain the origin of life on Earth involves a kind of hot spring on the ocean floor, called a hydrothermal vent. Tiny enclosures of rock about the size of large cells provide ideal environments for 'breeding' complex organic chemicals.

MIND BOGGLER

● The renowned American astrophysicist and science writer Carl Sagan said the Miller-Urey experiments were 'the single most significant step in convincing many scientists that life is likely to be abundant in the cosmos.'

Colour TV

In the 1950s, television technology was sufficiently reliable for regular colour television broadcasts to begin. An organisation in the USA called the National Television Standards Council (NTSC) set out details for a standard colour television signal. In the NTSC format – still used today – the colour signal is broadcast alongside the black and white one. The existing sets would not pick up the colour signal and could watch as normal. But the new sets would overlay the colour image. The standard in Britain, which has the same feature, is called PAL (phase alternating line). Colour transmissions in Britain began in 1967.

Black smoker This hydrothermal vent is home to many 'extremophile' organisms, that thrive in the hot, dark, sulphurous conditions. Life on Earth may have begun at one of these vents.

NOW JUMP TO... ◗ DARWIN page 64; ◗ DNA page 112; ◗ ALIEN CONTACT page 138

THE Sun

Saturday, May 16, 1953   2d

FREE

TIN OF PRIMORDIAL SOUP FOR EVERY READER

SEE PAGE 32

NOW with added LIFE!

RIMORDIAL SOUP

AT LAST, TELLY IN COLOUR

COLOUR TV is set to be launched, The Sun can reveal. America's broadcasting watch-dogs have finally approved it after years of wrangling.

The first sets (pictured above) go on sale in December — though it may be years before Britain gets any.

Footie: Greys v Whites — Back Page

'I'M STAN ALMIGHTY

student creates new life'...out of nothing

By JENNY SIS

A 23-YEAR-OLD student called Stan has created "life" from nothing in a science lab, it was revealed last night.

Stanley Miller, 23, mixed chemicals in flasks to simulate the "primordial soup" on the early Earth.

Then he blasted them with sparks, like the constant lightning storms which once blitzed the planet.

The experiment went on non-stop for a week.

FLUKE

Afterwards Stanley and his Professor Harold Urey, 60, noticed the flasks now contained amino acids, the "building blocks of life."

The experiment at Chicago University proves that the earliest life on Earth may well have been produced by a fluke set of chemical reactions, rather than from another form of life already present.

Last night Stan said what he'd done was **EASY**. He said: "The fact the experiment is so simple a high school student can almost reproduce it is not a negative at all. The fact that it works and is so simple is what is so great about it."

Stan To Have Day Of Rest — Page 9

Godlike . . . brilliant student Stan in action

1967 THE OPERATION THAT SHOOK THE WORLD

THE human heart has always been a source of wonder. So it is not surprising that the world's first human heart transplant, by the South African surgeon Christiaan Barnard, made both patient and surgeon celebrities overnight.

The successful, routine transplantation of whole organs requires a sophisticated understanding of the human body and modern surgical techniques. One advance in surgery that made them possible was the joining, or suturing, of severed blood vessels. The first practical technique was developed by French surgeon Alexis Carrel (1873–1944) in the early 1900s.

Transplant surgery presents a special challenge: the threat of rejection. Since the transplanted organ is generally from another person, the recipient's immune system may attack it and this can severely harm the patient. The risk of rejection can be reduced, however, by suppressing the immune system using drugs appropriately called immunosuppressants.

Donor organs are 'typed' or 'cross-matched' – undergoing laboratory tests that examine the potential risk of them being rejected by the recipient's antibodies. Identical twins are guaranteed a match: the body will behave as if the organ

Cardiac surgery Reconstruction of a modern operating theatre, with surgeons and assistants carrying out open heart surgery. The risks involved in procedures like this are very much reduced compared with a hundred years ago.

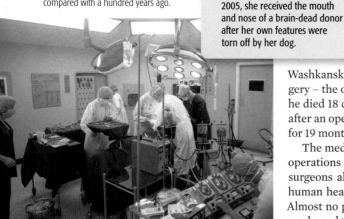

Artificial heart This plastic and metal heart (2000) is designed as a replacement for the human heart, when no donor organ is available. Researchers hope this technology will become routine in the next ten years.

was already its own. The science behind cross-matching developed gradually during the 20th century, beginning with the discovery of blood types by Karl Landsteiner (1868–1943).

The human immune system is incredibly complex and still not fully understood. In 1950, the Brazilian-born English physician Peter Medawar (1915–1987) discovered how the body distinguishes between its own and foreign tissues. As a result, surgeons began human organ transplants in earnest, although they did not become routine until the mid-1960s.

A team headed by American surgeon Norman Shumway (b. 1923) successfully carried out a heart transplant in a dog in 1958. Donated hearts tend to be rejected more often and more easily than most other organs; Shumway spent the next decade working on ways to suppress the recipient's immune system.

Barnard (1922–2001) also carried out successful heart transplants in dogs during the 1960s before trying the operation on his first human patient, Louis Washkansky (1913–1967). Washkansky was terminally ill – he would have died within weeks with his existing heart. The donor heart came from a woman killed in a road accident. Washkansky was awake and cheerful after surgery – the operation had been successful – but he died 18 days later. Barnard's second patient, after an operation a few months later, survived for 19 months.

The media attention surrounding Barnard's operations created a buzz among patients and surgeons alike. Within a year, more than 100 human heart transplants had been completed. Almost no patients survived longer than a few weeks and the buzz died down. People began to question the ethics of spending large amounts of time and money on these operations when patients had such a limited life span.

A few surgeons – Barnard and Shumway in particular – persevered through the 1970s, improving the immunosuppressant drugs and the post-operative care to the point where more than half the patients lived relatively normal lives for five years or more.

In 1981, the first successful heart-lung transplant took place at Stanford University Hospital in California.

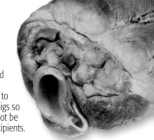

Pig's heart Animal organs have been successfully transplanted into human patients – notably from pigs and chimpanzees. Some researchers are trying to genetically engineer pigs so that their hearts will not be rejected in human recipients.

MIND BOGGLER

● Nearly 30 years after the first heart transplant, Frenchwoman Isabelle Dinoire was the recipient of the first FACE transplant. On 27th November 2005, she received the mouth and nose of a brain-dead donor after her own features were torn off by her dog.

Supersonic airliner

Concorde was expensive, noisy and controversial, but it had a special place in the hearts of many people. It was the first supersonic (faster than sound) passenger airliner. It cruised at 2,179 kilometres per hour (1,354 mph). Concorde, the French word for 'agreement', was a joint project between aircraft companies in Britain and France. It was completed by 1969 and went into regular service in 1975. Sixteen were made. Concorde was retired in 2003.

WHAT IN THE WORLD?

1953 The coronation of Queen Elizabeth II (b. 1926).
1953 Edmund Hillary (b. 1919) and Tenzing Norgay (1914–1986) become the first to reach the summit of Mount Everest.
1953 American physicist Charles Townes (1915) develops the maser, precursor to the laser.
1956 English engineer Christopher Cockerell (1910–1999) builds the first practical hovercraft.
1956 The first transatlantic telephone cable begins operation.
1957 High-speed modern dental drill is introduced.
1957 The first artificial satellite, Sputnik I, is launched from Russia.
1959 The first commercial photocopier goes on sale.
1960 Theodore Maiman (b. 1927) builds the first working laser.
1962 The Cuban missile crisis brings USA and Russia to brink of nuclear war.
1962 Telstar, a U.S. communications satellite, relays television pictures and telephone signals across the Atlantic Ocean.
1963 Assassination of President John F. Kennedy.
1963 Syncom 2 becomes the first satellite in geosynchronous orbit (it always remains in the same spot in the sky viewed from Earth).
1963 Valentina Tereshkova (b. 1937) becomes the first woman in space.
1965 Measles vaccine is developed.

NOW JUMP TO... ◔ ANATOMY page 30; ◔ PASTEUR page 66

THE Sun

Monday, December 4, 1967   4d

CONK-ORDE
Pointy-nose jet unveiled

THIS is Concorde, the incredible pointy-nosed jet that will fly passengers faster than the speed of sound.

Although it is still two years from launch, The Sun was allowed a sneak preview of the aircraft being built in Filton, Bristol. It is unlike any plane ever seen.

And it will be able to fly to New York from London in 3½ hours, which thanks to the time difference means passengers will get there BEFORE they set off!

BRITISH AIRCRAFT CORPORATION — AEROSPATIALE FRANCE

G-BSST   Concorde

FULL AMAZING STORY: PAGE 9

HEART SWAP MIRACLE

First successful transplant op stuns world

Miracle man . . . Washkansky before op

By CHESTER CAVITY

THE first ever successful heart transplant stunned the world last night.

Top surgeon Christiaan Barnard performed the nine-hour op in Cape Town, South Africa.

His patient, grocer Louis Washkansky, 55, received the heart of a young woman killed in a road crash. He was still alive last night — and the heart was working.

Dashing Dr Barnard, 45, is now poised for global stardom. He said: "My goal is to alleviate suffering."

Full Story — Page 5

Surgeon . . Barnard

1969 SPACE RACE AND MOON LANDING

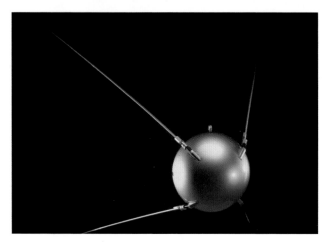

AS he set foot on the moon, astronaut Neil Armstrong described the achievement as a 'giant leap' for mankind. It is still arguably our greatest technological feat. And it was brought about by a 'space race' resulting from the bitter Cold War between Russia and America from the 1950s until the 1980s.

In the years after World War II, military engineers in the USA and Russia carried out a number of high-altitude rocket test flights alongside specialists who had worked at the Germans' wartime missile development centre Peenemunde. The aim was part military, but part scientific too.

The Cold War between the two superpowers began, and they battled for political, economic and military supremacy. Both also started to pour vast sums into space technology.

There was no exchange of knowledge so the Americans were taken by surprise when, on October 4th 1957, the Russian space agency launched a spacecraft into orbit: Sputnik 1. A month later Sputnik 2 carried the first animal into space: a dog named Laika.

The Sputnik programme shook the U.S. government into action. In 1958, they created the National Aeronautics and Space

MIND BOGGLER

- Neil Armstrong fluffed one of history's most momentous lines. He had intended to say 'One small step for a man, one giant leap for mankind' when he stepped on to the moon. But the 'a' was never heard. It is possible it was smothered by radio interference – though Armstrong admits he may have simply forgotten it.

First steps Sputnik 1, Earth's artificial satellite. Launched in 1957, it had a mass of 83.8 kilograms (a weight of 184 lb). The long metal spikes are radio antennas.

Administration (NASA) and the American space programme began to gather momentum. NASA launched a number of satellites between 1959 and 1963. However, the USA fell further behind when on April 12th 1961 Russian cosmonaut Yuri Gagarin (1934–1968) became the first human in space. The Americans' first astronaut Alan Shepard (1923–1998) went up less than a month later.

The same year, U.S. president John F Kennedy (1917–1963) announced his intention that his country would put a man on the moon before the end of the decade. The Russians were not so set on sending people there. They sent unmanned probes instead: Luna 1 flew past the moon as early as 1959 and by 1966, Luna 9 completed a 'soft' lunar landing. The USA was sending unmanned probes too – but with the sole purpose of preparing for a manned mission. The Russians did eventually begin preparations to send a man to the moon – but this time the Americans got there first.

The American project was the Apollo Program. NASA decided it would put into lunar orbit a modular spacecraft carrying three astronauts. The craft would divide in two: the 'lunar module' would descend to the surface with two astronauts while the 'command/service module' would stay in orbit around the moon piloted by the other one.

The Apollo missions were put into space by the biggest, most powerful launch vehicle ever made: the rocket Saturn V. With each mission, NASA moved a step closer to their goal. Finally, on July 20th 1969 (the early hours of July 21st in Britain) – with Buzz Aldrin (b. 1930) behind him and Michael Collins (b. 1930) in the Command/Service Module – Armstrong (b. 1930) became the first person to step onto the moon's surface. That was Apollo 11. The last

Saturn V The launch vehicle of choice for NASA's Apollo Program was the Saturn V. It was a three-stage rocket that stood more than 100 metres (320 ft) tall.

manned mission to the moon was Apollo 17. It left there on December 17th 1972. In the 1980s, political changes, mainly in Russia, reduced tensions between the two countries and ended the Cold War. The Space Race had fizzled out by then, too.

Moon shot The Lunar Module of Apollo 11 after lifting off from the moon's surface. Photograph taken by Michael Collins, from lunar orbit in the Command/Service Module.

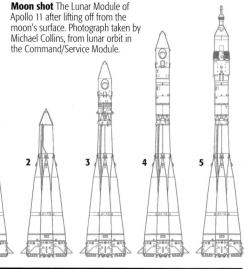

The development of Russian launch rockets, 1957–1966. **1** is the R-7, an ICBM; **2** is the 8K71PS, which launched Sputnik; **3** is the 8K72K, which carried Yuri Gagarin; **4** is the 11A57 Voskhod (3KV) launcher; **5** is the 11A511, 49.3 metres (161 ft) tall.

WHAT IN THE WORLD?

1967 The modern definition of a 'second' is agreed as 9,192,631,770 9 192 631 770 periods of the radiation corresponding to the transition between the two hyperfine levels of the ground state of the caesium-133 atom.

1967 Direct dialling is introduced between the Britain and the USA.

1967 Charles Yanofsky (b. 1925) and his team work out how DNA builds proteins in cells.

1968 The first oil supertankers go into service.

NOW JUMP TO... ◀ ROCKETRY page 82; ▶ MARS PROBES page120

THE Sun

Monday, July 21, 1969 — 6d

2.56am TODAY . . . THE HISTORIC STATEMENT OF NEIL ARMSTRONG, FIRST HUMAN TO SET FOOT ON THE MOON

One small step for man, one giant leap for mankind

FULL STORY: PAGES 2-33

BEYOND THE MOON: EXPLORING SPACE

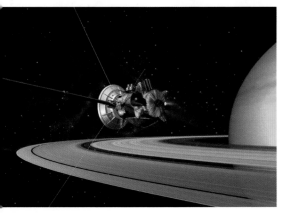

Probe in flight This artist's impression of the space probe Cassini, an orbiter which arrived at Saturn in 2004. Cassini carried a small probe, Huygens, which descended to the surface of Saturn's biggest moon, Titan.

THROUGHOUT the summer of 1976, people around the world were transfixed as two unmanned American space vehicles approached Mars. On board each was a 'lander', which descended to the surface and sent back spectacular pictures of the Red Planet. Now, more than ever, space probes are providing us with thrilling glimpses of worlds beyond our own.

Human explorers need food, water, air, sanitation and shelter from the extremely harsh and airless environment of space. Unmanned spacecraft only need a source of electricity, which can be generated by radioactive heating or solar cells. There are many different types of unmanned craft, including communications and weather satellites, satellites for observing Earth and space telescopes. Most exciting are space probes, which make long journeys to other planets and moons.

No humans have been more than a few hundred kilometres from Earth since the last Apollo moon mission in 1972. But unmanned probes have travelled huge distances in our solar system. They have visited the sun, moon and every planet except Pluto. They have visited other moons, plus comets and asteroids.

The most basic mission is a fly-by. As it passes close to another world, a fly-by probe takes photographs and makes other measurements such as the magnetic field strength and surface temperature. This data is beamed back to Earth via radio signals. Alternatively, a probe may be put into orbit around a planet, where it can do the same over months or years. Then there are missions that send probes to make a landing millions of kilometres from Earth.

Sometimes, one mission has both an orbiter

and a lander. The orbiter can make useful measurements from high altitude while acting as a relay station for signals to and from the lander on the surface. NASA's Viking programme, launched in 1975, was just such a mission. The landers on Viking I and Viking II had sophisticated robot arms designed to collect Martian soil samples and deposit them in self-contained mini-laboratories. One aim was to look for evidence of life, but none was found. The landers also had a 'meteorology boom' – a small weather station that measured wind speed, and atmospheric temperature and pressure. They each had several cameras too.

The Viking orbiters also carried scientific apparatus and cameras and surveyed most of the planet's surface. Among the many thousands of photographs they took, one particularly caught the public's imagination. Nicknamed 'the Face on Mars', it is a geological feature that in certain light resembles a human face. Some people suggested it was evidence of an ancient Martian civilisation.

Unmanned probes – from NASA and, increasingly, other space agencies – continue to make incredible strides. NASA's Voyager 2 made its closest approach to Uranus in 1986 and Neptune in 1989. Its goal is to leave the solar system – and it is expected to transmit data into the 2030s.

The European Space Agency's Huygens probe surveyed Saturn before landing on its moon Titan in 2005, sending back data for 90 minutes. The ESA's Venus Express is currently orbiting Venus.

Mars is being orbited by four spacecraft and has

Jupiter close-up Photograph of Jupiter's 'Great Red Spot' – a huge storm bigger than Earth – taken in 1979, by Voyager 1, which also visited Saturn. Voyager 2 also went to Uranus and Neptune.

NASA's two Mars Exploration Rovers on its surface. A NASA mission named Messenger will eventually orbit Mercury in 2011 and NASA's Juno spacecraft is due to launch by 2010 on a mission to orbit Jupiter.

Pluto, the one planet in our solar system yet to be visited, is the destination for NASA's New Horizons probe, which launched in January 2006 and should arrive in 2015.

Soil sample View of the Martian surface, with the Viking 2 lander in the foreground. The soil sampling arm is visible in the centre.

NOW JUMP TO... ● ROCKETRY page 82; ● MOON LANDINGS page 118; ● MARS COLONY page 134

THE Sun

Wednesday, July 21, 1976   10p

Did Martians carve this?

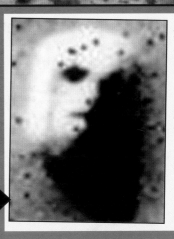

AN astonishing picture which seems to be of a human face has been sent back from Mars by Viking I.

NASA insists it is a rock formation which only looks human because our brains tend to "form" faces from unusual shapes.

But Sun space expert Ron Endastick said: "I am certain this is a gigantic 'greeting' carved for us by an ancient civilisation which has long since died out in a Martian nuclear war."

VIKING ON MARS

(No, folks, it's not our cuddly hero Hagar!)

THIS is the dramatic first picture from Mars, beamed to Earth last night after the Viking lander touched down.

The image shows a

By ROCKY BADLANDS

dusty red wasteland strewn with rocks.

There is no immediate sign of life, or water — nor of our own cuddly cartoon Viking, Hagar the Horrible! NASA's Viking I, about the size of a

British Leyland Mini, launched from Cape Canaveral, Florida, last August.

Aside from taking pictures, the lander has instruments for studying Mars's surface and atmosphere. A second probe, Viking II, lands on the Red Planet in September.

Voyage to Mars . . . Viking's launch last year

COULD WE BE MEN FROM MARS? Pages 4&5

● 121

PLUTO

HABITABILITY RATING 2/10

TINY, distant, frozen planet less than a fifth of Earth's diameter. Atmosphere: Methane, nitrogen, carbon dioxide. Ave temp -229˚C. Gravity: 5% Earth's. Closest distance from Earth: 2.67 billion miles. Little is known for sure.

NEPTUNE

HABITABILITY RATING 0/10

GAS giant four times Earth's diameter. Liquid surface. Storms of unimaginable ferocity. Atmosphere: Hydrogen, helium, methane, ammonia. Ave temp: -220˚C. Gravity: 114% Earth's. Closest distance from Earth: 2,691m miles.

JUPITER

HABITABILITY RATING 0/10

LARGEST planet — a ball of dust, hydrogen, helium, methane, water and ammonia 1,300 times Earth's volume. Average temp: -148˚C. Gravity 250% Earth's. Closest distance from Earth: 370m miles. Probably has no solid surface.

COULD WE BE MEN FROM MARS?

...or Mercury, Venus, Pluto or Titan

THE Sun today asks a question vital to mankind's future: Can we live on other planets?

The Viking probe's pictures reveal Mars as ripe for colonisation.

And, as Earth's resources run out, another planet may be our only hope, especially if it can be transformed over centuries to support us.

Here, The Sun's space expert Terry Formin assesses the possibilities: "Wherever we went we'd initially need

By COLIN IZASHAN

life-supporting buildings to protect us from heat, cold, radiation and toxic gases. Even then, some places are non-starters: **Neptune, Jupiter, Saturn** and **Uranus** don't even have a solid surface.

"**Venus** is near us and has similar gravity but it's like a furnace and has no water.

"**Pluto** is 2.6billion miles away — we're not going there in a hurry. **Mercury** may be habitable at its icy poles but elsewhere it's hot enough to melt lead. A

decent bet is **Europa**, a moon of Jupiter, with a crust of ice and an ocean beneath. But its radiation is fatal.

"Saturn's moon **Titan** is better. It has an atmosphere, many Earth-like features and possibly an ocean.

"Our **Moon** is a favourite because it's so close — but it's got high radiation, temperature extremes and a huge risk of meteor strikes.

"**Mars** is much more likely. It's not far away, probably has water and its conditions match some of the extremes on Earth. One day this could be our new home."

URANUS

HABITABILITY RATING 0/10

GAS giant, no solid surface, four times Earth's diameter. Atmosphere: hydrogen, helium, methane. Has two ring systems around it. Ave temp –214˚C. Gravity: 117% Earth's. Closest distance from Earth: 1,614m miles.

MERCURY

HABITABILITY RATING 2/10

DUSTY cratered planet nearest to the sun, two-fifths size of Earth. Temperature variation -210˚C to 510˚C. Thin atmosphere, mainly helium. Gravity: 38% of Earth's. Closest distance from Earth: 48m miles.

SATURN

HABITABILITY RATING 0/10

SECOND largest planet, ten Earths in diameter, known for its rings of ice. Atmosphere: hydrogen/helium. Ave temp -140˚C. Closest distance from Earth: 748m miles. Gravity 107% Earth's. Surface: Liquid and gas.

EUROPA

HABITABILITY RATING 3/10

ICEBOUND moon of Jupiter about a quarter of Earth's diameter and with 13% of its gravity. Has a very thin atmosphere of oxygen, produced as sunlight evaporates its ice crust. Average temperature: -153°C. Closest distance from Earth: 370million miles.

VENUS

HABITABILITY RATING 3/10

WATERLESS expanse of mountains, canyons and plains about 95% size of Earth. Dense atmosphere, mainly carbon dioxide, creates greenhouse effect and temperatures of 400°C. Gravity 90% Earth's. Closest distance from Earth: 26m miles.

MARS

HABITABILITY RATING 9/10

DUSTY red planet of canyons, dunes, volcanoes and polar ice caps made of frozen carbon dioxide and water. Mars is about half Earth's size but has almost as much dry land. Atmosphere is mainly carbon dioxide. Temperature range: -140°C to 20°C. Gravity about 38% of Earth's. Closest distance from Earth: 35 million miles.

TITAN

HABITABILITY RATING 6/10

MOON of Saturn, 45% of Earth's diameter, with a surface of water and rock. Has 38% Earth's gravity and a dense nitrogen-rich atmosphere. Is totally covered by fog of methane. Ave temp: -180°C. Closest distance from Earth: 747m miles.

MOON

HABITABILITY RATING 7/10

OUR nearest neighbour, a pock-marked rock a quarter of Earth's diameter with no atmosphere. Its temperature ranges from 130°C in sunlight to -110°C in darkness. Average distance from Earth: 238,857 miles. Gravity: 16% of Earth's.

1978 LOUISE, THE BABY CONCEIVED IN A LAB

BEFORE 25th July 1978, everyone ever born had been conceived in the natural way: with sperm and an egg combining inside a woman's uterus. But Louise Brown, born at 11:47pm that day, was conceived outside the body as a result of in vitro fertilisation (IVF). By 2006, more than three million babies worldwide had been born through the same amazing procedure.

In the 1960s the English physician Robert Edwards (b. 1925) became interested in human fertilisation after studying animal reproduction and genetics. IVF – fertilising an egg outside the body – had already been used in animals for years. The embryos that result from IVF are transferred or 'implanted' into the uterus, and animals give birth in the normal way.

Edwards became aware of the plight of women who are unable to conceive naturally because of damage or disease in their fallopian tubes. Blockages in these tubes prevent eggs from the ovaries ever meeting the sperm making their way up from the uterus. Edwards realised human IVF could help.

In 1968 he fertilised a human egg in a glass dish for the first time. The resulting embryo grew to a tiny mass of cells called a blastocyst.

Before he could develop the technique any further he had to find a way of obtaining eggs from a patient. Edwards read about a surgical procedure called laparoscopy in a scientific paper written by the English gynaecologist Patrick Steptoe (1913–1988). Laparoscopy provides a way for surgeons to observe the inside of a patient's abdomen – and in some cases carry out simple surgery – using only a minimal incision. The technique had existed since the early 1900s but Steptoe pioneered its use in gynaecology.

Edwards realised laparoscopic techniques would enable him to retrieve eggs from women's ovaries and he and Steptoe began to work together.

As a gynaecologist, Steptoe was able to find several couples unable to conceive naturally who were interested in trying the new technique. After a few false starts – and severe criticism of the procedure as immoral or unsafe – he and Edwards finally had success with Lesley and John Brown, who had been trying to conceive for several years. Louise Brown was born at Oldham General Hospital amid huge media interest.

The technique Steptoe and Edwards pioneered now helps couples who are infertile for many reasons, not just due to blocked fallopian tubes.

Several important developments have added to the range and effectiveness of IVF – each controversial in its own way. For example, using ICSI (intra-cytoplasmic sperm injection), an IVF technician injects an individual sperm directly into an egg under a microscope.

Another technique is the freezing of 'spare' embryos. If an implanted embryo fails to go to term, the couple having treatment can have another attempt without having to start the whole procedure from scratch. If their first attempt does succeed, the frozen embryo gives them a good chance of having a second child if they wish.

Finally, pre-implantation genetic diagnosis (PGD) enables IVF doctors to implant only 'healthy' embryos. This procedure is only used for couples with a history of a severe genetic disease. In these rare cases, IVF is also available to couples who would have little trouble conceiving.

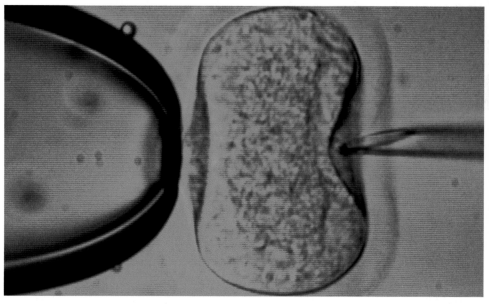

Making a baby Microscopic view of the ICSI technique, showing a needle (right) being used to inject a sperm into the egg. The large glass pipette (left) holds the egg still. ICSI can help to overcome problems with sperm with low 'motility'.

MIND BOGGLER

● A couple's course of IVF at a clinic in Leeds led to mixed-race twins in 2000 after the father's sperm sample became mixed up with that of an Asian man. The couple ended up having to legally adopt their own children.

Pluto's moon

In June 1978, American astronomer James Christy (b. 1938) discovered Pluto's moon, which was temporarily named S/1978 P 1 until Christy named it 'Charon', pronouncing it 'sh' after his wife's name. Its diameter is about half that of its parent planet. In 2005, two more moons were discovered orbiting Pluto; they were named Nix and Hydra.

Robert Edwards (left) and **Patrick Steptoe**.

WHAT IN THE WORLD?

1976 Steve Jobs (b. 1955) and Steve Wozniak (b. 1950) found the Apple Computer Company.

1976 IBM introduces the first laser printer.

1977 NASA launches space probes Voyager 1, which visited Jupiter and Saturn, and Voyager 2, which visited those planets and Uranus and Neptune.

1977 Concorde begins regular flights between London and New York.

Grown up Louise Brown, the first person born as a result of IVF, has grown up perfectly normal and healthy.

NOW JUMP TO... ◄ ANATOMY page 30; ► CLONING page 130

A NEW moon of Pluto has been discovered — and astronomers are calling it SHARON.

U.S. stargazer James Christy found the satellite (right in our picture) and named it Charon, a figure from Greek myth.

But he plans to pronouce it "Sh" — after his wife Charlene.

Find 'Tracey' — Page 2

NEW MOON CALLED SHARON!

TOT FROM A TEST TUBE!

First baby born after new 'IVF' treatment

Pioneer . . . Louise last night shortly after miraculous 'IVF' birth

SAY hello to Louise Brown, the first baby ever born following "in-vitro fertilisation".

The historic "test tube" tot came into the world at Oldham General Hospital, Lancs, at 11.47pm last night weighing 5lb 12oz.

Mum Lesley and dad John went through the pioneering medical treatment after nine years of trying in vain for a

By BERTHA STONISHING

baby. The delicate IVF procedure involved taking an egg from Lesley, mixing it with John's sperm in a laboratory and implanting the resulting embryo in Lesley's womb.

Louise's birth could pave the way for thousands of infertile couples to have babies. But IVF, developed by doctors Patrick Steptoe and Robert Edwards, has upset religious leaders.

Full Story — Pages 4 & 5

● 125

1984 CDs, DAWN OF THE DIGITAL REVOLUTION

THE introduction of the compact disc, or CD, was the beginning of a 'digital revolution' which now dominates electronic media.

Introduced in 1982, the CD was slow to catch on. The sound was crisp and clear and the discs did not scratch as easily as vinyl records. But people had to buy new machines to play them – and were reluctant to replace their record collections.

Despite the slow start, people did start buying the discs and their players, especially when prices began to fall and major stars began to release albums on the new media. By 1988, sales of (digital) CDs had outstripped sales of (analogue) records. Since then (digital) DVD has largely superseded (analogue) videocassette for delivering films.

The wavy groove of a record is a direct representation (an analogue) of sound waves. In digital technology, sound waves are represented by a succession of binary numbers instead. On the underside of a CD is a spiral track containing tiny indentations which represent the digits 0 and 1. This is scanned by a laser in the CD player and decoded into sound.

The quality of recorded sound on a CD is very high. But something very close to CD quality can be recorded using far fewer binary digits per second – a smaller amount of digital information. This led to the development of compressed audio formats, notably the 'mp3' (MPEG layer 3). Images and video can also be 'digitised' – converted into a stream of binary digits.

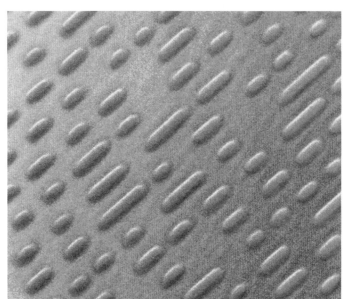

Zeros and ones This scanning electron microscope view of the underside of a CD shows the tiny pits that represent the binary numbers of a digital audio signal. The pits are aligned along a continuous spiral track that is 'read' by a laser.

MIND BOGGLER

● The binary data on a CD is arranged along a track 5.3 kilometres (3.3 miles) long, running from the inside of the disc to the outside edge.

The increasing popularity of the personal computer in the late 1980s and 1990s did much to encourage the uptake of digital technology. As processing power increased, personal computers became able to manipulate the large numbers of binary digits required for computer-based 'multimedia'.

Today, most people receive digital television signals; they speak on digital mobile telephones; they capture and share digital photographs and video; they listen to digital music on CD, on their computers or on mp3 players. Whether they are carrying sound, text, images, video, or a combination of all four, all digital technologies are doing is manipulating streams of binary digits.

Multimedia machine The Apple iPod, first introduced in 2001, has a large-capacity hard disk that can hold digitised music. Later models, like the one shown, also store and display still images, and even video.

Major player Philips began development of the compact disc in the late 1970s, and joined forces with Sony in 1979 to define the CD standards. This Philips CD player was introduced in 1983.

DNA fingerprinting

The invention of DNA fingerprinting by the English geneticist Alec Jeffreys (b. 1950) revolutionised forensic science. DNA can be recovered from a person's cells found at the scene of a crime. These cells are found in flakes of skin, blood and saliva and other bodily fluids. Today, Jeffreys' technology is used routinely in court. It is also used in disputes over paternity and by biologists carrying out genetic studies.

The technique employs molecules called restriction enzymes, which cut DNA at certain points. The resulting fragments are different lengths for every individual (except identical twins). An electric field is used to separate them according to length and the result is a unique pattern that looks like a supermarket barcode.

Thames Barrier

The Thames Barrier, opened in 1984, was designed to protect London and the South East of England from the threat of flooding until at least 2030. Construction, across a 523-metre wide stretch, began in 1974. Protection became a particular concern after the deaths of 307 people in floods in 1953.

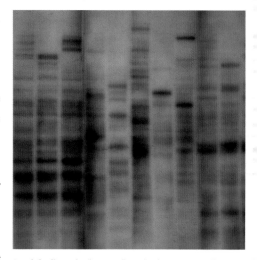

Read the lines The first DNA figerprint, from 1984. Small radioactive 'markers' were attached to the fragments of DNA, so that they would show up on photographic paper. Today, phosphorescent markers are used.

WHAT IN THE WORLD?

1979 Margaret Thatcher (b. 1925) becomes Britain's first female Prime Minister.

1980 The Mount St Helens volcano (Washington State, USA) erupts spectacularly.

1980 John Lennon murdered.

1981 The launch of the first fully-functional Space Shuttle, *Columbia*.

1981 The invention of the scanning tunnelling microscope.

1982 The Falklands War between Britain and Argentina.

1983 The first commercial mobile phone is available.

NOW JUMP TO... ⮐ THE LIGHTBULB page 70; ⮐ COMPUTERS page 110

THE Sun

Tuesday, September 11, 1984   16p

LONDON SAFE TILL 2030

By HUGH BRIS

LONDON is safe from a catastrophic flood until at least 2030, it was revealed last night. The Thames Barrier, opened earlier this year, can keep the capital safe for 46 years at the present rate the tide is rising. Only an unforeseen disaster could overwhelm it. The barrier was first dreamed up in 1953 after floods killed 300.

Another Scorcher — Page 15

Turning the tide . . . the magnificent new Thames Barrier can't be breached for almost half a century

rt Alec . . . Jeffreys

ell-tale lues n DNA o nail rooks

By IVOR LEED

OOKS could soon trapped by their DNA.

scientist at Leices* University is develg "genetic fingerting", which uld be a foolproof of proving guilt. eryone's DNA is que, except that of tical twins. So if a pect's DNA matches t of a crime scene ple, it MUST mean were involved.

rofessor Alec Jefs, 34, made the overy at 9.05am terday. "Suddenly I d see the potenfor individual idenation," he said.

KILLERS' URY AT CHEATS'

EE PAGE 11

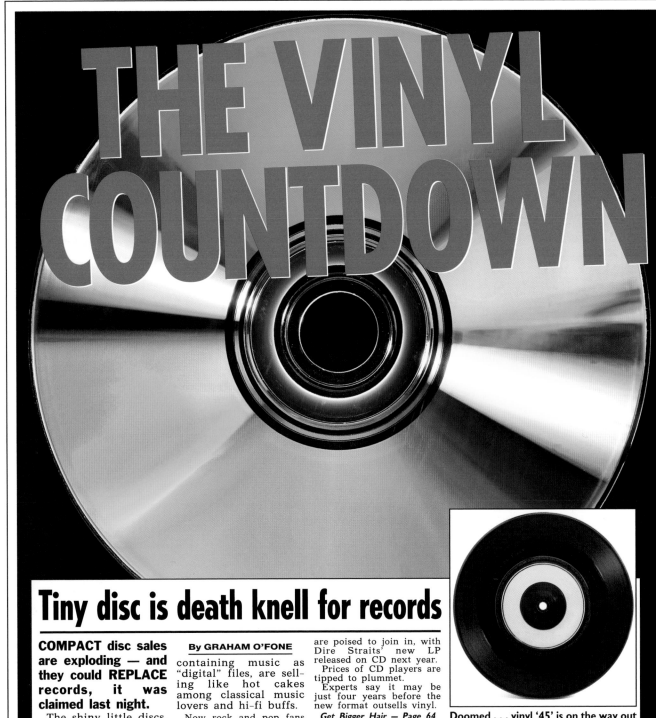

Tiny disc is death knell for records

By GRAHAM O'FONE

COMPACT disc sales are exploding — and they could **REPLACE** records, it was claimed last night.

The shiny little discs, containing music as "digital" files, are selling like hot cakes among classical music lovers and hi-fi buffs.

Now rock and pop fans are poised to join in, with Dire Straits' new LP released on CD next year.

Prices of CD players are tipped to plummet.

Experts say it may be just four years before the new format outsells vinyl.

Get Bigger Hair — Page 64

Doomed . . . vinyl '45' is on the way out

1991 A MODERN INVENTION TO CHANGE OUR LIVES

THE WORLD Wide Web, invented quietly and almost single-handedly by British computer scientist Tim Berners-Lee, has brought about a global communications revolution unprecedented in human history. It gives people in every country access to billions of documents carrying information, ideas and images, as well as to 'online' services such as shopping and banking.

Although the Internet came to the public's attention in the 1990s, its roots lie further back. In the late 1950s all computers were 'mainframes' which fed individual terminals, normally in the same building. But a few academics had terminals a long way from the mainframe, connected via dedicated telephone lines. By the end of the 1960s, mainframes in different locations were connected – becoming the first computer networks.

During the 1970s there were several networks, across which academics or military personnel shared information. The 'backbone' of the Internet was created when these were linked up. This was a challenge because each had its own way of manipulating and transmitting information, known as a protocol.

In the late 1970s American computer sci-

Web of one This is the computer on which Tim Berners-Lee wrote the first web page, in 1991.

entists Robert Kahn (b. 1938) and Vint Cerf (b. 1943) developed a way for different networks to communicate, called TCP/IP (transfer and control protocol/internetworking protocol). Every computer on the Internet had a unique number assigned to it, its IP address.

Academics in several countries were now connected, exchanging information via 'bulletin boards'. In the late 1980s, non-academics with personal computers were able to connect to the Internet too, via Internet Service Providers (ISPs).

Berners-Lee (b. 1955), from London, had already developed a program which enabled a user to click with their computer mouse on cross-references (or 'links') within a document and thus call up automatically another document they referred to. This became known as hypertext.

In 1989, while working at the Swiss headquarters of the European nuclear and particle physics research facility CERN, he drew up plans to link the hypertext idea with the Internet. The idea was to allow researchers to share ideas and results without constantly exchanging e-mail. They could place information 'online', where it could be viewed by their colleagues at any time.

Berners-Lee invented a set of rules all computers would be able to follow, called hypertext transfer protocol (HTTP). He also invented a computer 'language', hypertext markup language (HTML), for creating web pages with hypertext links. The final piece of the jigsaw was the uniform resource locator (URL). Instead of a link just calling up a file on the same computer, they were 'universal', allowing use over a global Web. Every web page, image, sound and other type of file available on the Web has a unique URL.

Berners-Lee also wrote the software for the first Web server (a 'bank' storing files to be shared) and the first Web 'browser' (the program to access and display the server's files).

The Web, as it became known, was made publicly available during the summer of 1991. According to the latest figures, it is used regularly by more than one billion people.

Inspect a gadget The BlackBerry allows handheld, wireless access to email and the Web – as well as being a mobile phone, calendar, address book…

MIND BOGGLER

- Search engines such as Google have become indispensable tools for many Web users. But most of the estimated 550 billion current Web pages are in the 'deep Web', invisible to search engines.

WHAT IN THE WORLD?

1984 Apple computers releases its first Macintosh computer, with a fully-functioning graphical user interface (GUI).

1985 English inventor and entrepreneur Clive Sinclair (b. 1940) introduces his innovative but short-lived C5 personal vehicle. Only 17,000 were sold.

1986 The Russian nuclear power plant at Chernobyl explodes – the worst nuclear accident in history.

1986 Seven astronauts are killed when Space Shuttle *Challenger* explodes 73 seconds after lift-off.

1989 The fall of the Berlin Wall leads the way for German reunification.

1990 Space Shuttle *Discovery* places the Hubble Space Telescope into orbit.

British astronaut

English chemist Helen Sharman (b. 1963) was the first Briton in space, spending eight days aboard the Russian Mir space station. Mir was a modular space station in low-Earth orbit. The first piece was launched in 1986. From space, Sharman took photographs of Britain and spoke via radio to British schoolchildren.

NOW JUMP TO… ◀ PRINTING page 22; ▶ COMPUTERS page 110

THE Sun

Monday, May 20, 1991   25p

World Wide What?

COMPUTER 'WEB' TO CHANGE BILLIONS OF LIVES (YEAH, RIGHT)

By DOT COMME

A BRITISH computer geek's brainwave could be one of the greatest inventions ever, it was claimed last night.

Tim Berners-Lee, 35, has enabled computer users to see documents and pictures made available by others in "cyberspace".

He uses the "Internet" system, which so far only links academics but could eventually include anyone.

Berners-Lee, who works at a nuclear research base near Geneva, calls his idea the "World Wide Web".

One scientist said: "This could be huge. The idea of strangers worldwide sharing ideas instantly is mind-boggling." But another sneered: "They said Sinclair's C5 would change the world. Now you'd struggle to give one away."

Riddle of 'E' mail — Page 8

Web feat . . . Berners-Lee

SHE'S IN OR-BRIT

She's a star . . . Helen, ringed, boards the Soviet craft last night

Girl from Mars is our first astronaut

BRAVE Helen Sharman was enjoying being the first Briton in space yesterday after blasting off in a Soviet rocket.

Helen, 27, a chemist for sweets giant Mars, is also the first non-American or Soviet spacewoman in history. The Sheffield lass will spend eight days on the Mir space station.

She won her place on the mission in a radio contest which 13,000 people entered — and spent 18 months training for it at Star City in the Soviet Union.

Wish You Were Mir — Pages 6&7

1997 DOLLY THE SHEEP & CLONING TECHNOLOGY

IN the 1978 film 'The Boys from Brazil', Nazi scientists produce clones of Adolf Hitler: babies genetically identical to the former dictator. The film is science fiction, but some people felt the eerie scenario moved closer to reality when the birth of a female sheep called Dolly was announced in February 1997. She was the first ever clone of an adult mammal.

For thousands of years, people have been growing new plants by taking cuttings. The new plant is genetically identical to the existing one. Dolly was the animal equivalent of a cutting – although the procedure was much more complicated. She was born, after a normal pregnancy, at the Roslin Institute, Edinburgh, on July 5th 1996.

The embryo from which Dolly developed was made in an unusual way. Most cells of an adult animal contain a complete set of chromosomes in the nucleus. A human cell contains 46 in 23 pairs. Eggs and sperm cells are different: they contain only one member of each pair. When a human sperm enters an egg, it adds its 23 unpaired chromosomes to the 23 in the egg, making a new, unique combination with a full complement of 46.

Dolly was created using a different procedure called nuclear transfer. First, the scientists removed the nucleus from a ewe's egg – so that it contained

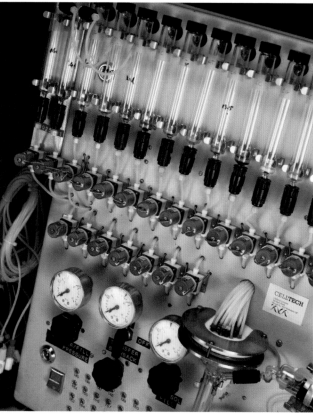

Genetic engineer This device is a 'DNA synthesiser' (1980s). It can produce short stretches of DNA to order, which can then be inserted into the chromosomes of target organisms, to endow the organisms with certain desired characteristics.

MIND BOGGLER

● *Jurassic Park* is the fictional account of dinosaurs being recreated from their DNA. But in real life, the 'Frozen Zoo', at the San Diego Zoo, California, contains stored cells from rare or endangered species so they can be cloned if they become extinct.

no chromosomes at all. Then they took a nucleus from a cell taken from an adult sheep – with a complete set of chromosomes – and inserted it into the 'empty' egg. The egg then behaved as if it had been fertilised. It began to divide, forming an embryo, which the researchers implanted into a ewe. Five months later Dolly was born. She was genetically identical to the sheep from which the cell was taken: an identical twin separated by a generation.

Dolly was created as part of research into genetic engineering, in which genes from one organism can be inserted into the chromosomes of another. This could result in a sheep that produces milk containing useful medical drugs, for example. Once the 'perfect' animal had been engineered, it could be cloned indefinitely.

Biologists cloned frogs in the 1950s. Mice

WHAT IN THE WORLD?

1992 The Maastricht Treaty is signed, forming the European Union.

1992 Pope John Paul issues an apology to Galileo Galilei on behalf of the Roman Catholic Church.

1994 The Channel Tunnel opens, after seven years of work.

1994 Astronomers watch closely as Comet Shoemaker-Levy 9 breaks up and fragments fall into the surface of Jupiter.

1997 Death of Princess Diana.

were cloned in the 1980s, although only by dividing embryos and implanting the two halves separately. Dolly was the first clone from an adult mammal cell. Her birth made headline news around the world. It raised moral questions, largely because Dolly was a mammal: if a sheep can be cloned, why not a human being? There is little justification for trying reproductive cloning in humans – for now, the risks remain too high. Nevertheless, there are those determined to go ahead, and the first human clone will probably be born this century.

One type of human cloning is being pursued by mainstream researchers: therapeutic cloning. This involves taking cells from a cloned embryo; it does not result in a new person. Part of an embryo is made of 'stem cells', which can develop into any kind of tissue. In the laboratory, embryonic stem cells can be nurtured to make living tissue – which could cause a revolution in medicine, treating conditions from burns to Parkinson's disease. In the future, scientists may be able to grow whole organs. The fact that the embryos are cloned from the patient means the laboratory-grown tissues and organs could be transplanted without rejection.

Home cloning kit Genetic engineering home cloning kit by Genemsco Corporation, USA.

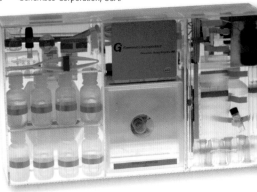

Copying an idea In 2003, the 'Raelian' religious cult claimed that it had produced a human clone, using this device, based on the technology used to make Dolly.

NOW JUMP TO... ◉ DNA page 112; ◉ FERTILITY TREATMENTS page 124

THE Sun

Monday, February 24, 1997   28p (buy one get one free)

CLONE SHOCK

Ewe copycat . . . cloned sheep Dolly last night. Her birth has caused huge ethical storm

Sheep Dolly first mammal 'copied' from adult animal

A SHEEP has been cloned, scientists announced last night.

The ewe, named Dolly, is the first mammal produced from an adult cell.

By JEAN COPPIE

She is named after busty country star Dolly Parton, because she was cloned from a mammary cell.

But the breakthrough at Edinburgh's Roslin Institute has caused fury.

It is feared if the technology is used on humans, a dictator could replace himself.

That would echo the nightmarish movie The Boys From Brazil, where mini-Hitlers were created.

I LOOK LIKE EWE: PAGES 4 & 5

THE Sun

Monday, February 24, 1997   28p (buy one get one free)

CLONE SHOCK

Ewe copycat . . . cloned sheep Dolly last night. Her birth has caused huge ethical storm

Sheep Dolly first mammal 'copied' from adult animal

A SHEEP has been cloned, scientists announced last night.

The ewe, named Dolly, is the first mammal produced from an adult cell.

By JEAN COPPIE

She is named after busty country star Dolly Parton, because she was cloned from a mammary cell.

But the breakthrough at Edinburgh's Roslin Institute has caused fury.

It is feared if the technology is used on humans, a dictator could replace himself.

That would echo the nightmarish movie The Boys From Brazil, where mini-Hitlers were created.

I LOOK LIKE EWE: PAGES 4 & 5

2034 THE SCIENCE OF CLIMATE CHANGE

GLOBAL warming is one of the biggest issues facing mankind. Aside from the potentially disastrous effects of dramatically changing weather patterns, the resulting rise in sea levels will threaten low-lying areas all over the world.

The average temperature of our atmosphere has risen by a small but significant 0.7° Celsius over the past 150 years. During the planet's 4.5 billion-year history the atmosphere has warmed and cooled much more than this – but the current rate of global warming is worryingly high.

Evidence from climate experts indicates that the increase is largely due to human activity. The main culprit is carbon dioxide, produced in huge quantities when we burn fossil fuels such as coal, gas and petrol. Trees absorb carbon dioxide: the more there are, the more carbon dioxide is kept out of the atmosphere – so massive deforestation is a major problem.

Carbon dioxide is a 'greenhouse gas'. Just as the temperature inside a greenhouse is higher than outside, an atmosphere containing greenhouse gases is warmer than one without them. But whereas a greenhouse works mostly by trapping air, the warming effect of greenhouse gases is due to the fact they absorb infrared radiation.

All warm objects emit infrared radiation – it is an important part of the way things cool down. The sun warms the Earth, and the Earth produces infrared, which escapes to space, keeping the planet cool – the whole system is in balance.

Greenhouse gases in the atmosphere stop some of the infrared radiation getting out. Without any such gases, Earth's average temperature would be –18° Celsius. The higher their concentration, the more infrared they

Save the planet Energy efficiency, and a switch to energy sources that don't produce greenhouse gases, such as wind power, can help to slow global warming.

block, and the slower the planet loses heat. As a result, the planet warms slightly and produces more infrared. Enough still escapes into space to counterbalance the warming effect of the sun but the temperature is nonetheless slightly higher.

As the planet warms, the sea rises. This is partly due to simple expansion – water takes up more space when it is warmer. But the melting of ice sheets, mostly in the Polar regions, is also very significant. Most ice around the North Pole is floating in the sea; when that melts, it makes no difference to sea levels because it is already displacing its own weight in the water. But the ice around the South Pole is land-based: it will increase sea levels as it melts.

The best estimates of global warming over the next 100 years suggest that sea level will rise by less than a metre – but this is enough to increase the risk of flooding dramatically for millions of people, including in some coastal areas of Britain.

London's Thames Barrier is the second largest 'moveable flood barrier' in the world. It was designed to help protect the UK's capital from high tides and storm surges until 2030. But it could fail before then if the planet continues to warm up.

Global warming is already changing weather patterns. Storms have become more fre-

Bleak future Polar bears are already suffering the effects of global warming. Sea ice around the North Pole makes up much of their habitat, and it is rapidly disappearing.

WHAT IN THE WORLD?

1999 The world's population hits 6 billion.
2001 Al Qaeda's 9/11 attacks on the USA.
2001 Apple releases its iPod music player.
2003 America and its Allies invade Iraq.
2003 Sequencing of the human genome – mapping our genes – is completed.
2004 The first privately-funded space flight, SpaceShipOne
2004 Tsunami in the Indian Ocean kills 310,000.
2004 Cassini-Huygens probe arrives at Saturn.
2005 The first face transplant, in France.
2006 NASA's New Horizons probe launched, bound for Pluto.

quent and more destructive because weather systems have more energy in a hotter atmosphere. Ocean currents that play a vital role in distributing heat around the world are being disturbed, resulting in droughts and famines in some areas and floods in others.

The world's climate is very complex. Scientists' best guesses of how it might develop over the next century could be wildly inaccurate. But current indications are that global temperature will continue rising – and the sea level with it.

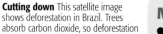

Cutting down This satellite image shows deforestation in Brazil. Trees absorb carbon dioxide, so deforestation is accelerating global warming.

MIND BOGGLER
● Europe's nine warmest years on record have all been since 1989 – and the summer of 2003 was the hottest for at least 500 years.

Invisible threat Every power station produces tonnes of carbon dioxide every day. The visible clouds in this photograph are steam, from the power station's cooling towers – the carbon dioxide is invisible.

NOW JUMP TO... ◆ THAMES BARRIER page 126

GIANT LEAPS

THE PALACE OF WETMINSTER

Parliament's under sea after tide of doom engulfs London

THIS was the scene of devastation at Westminster yesterday after the tide of death which engulfed London.

Thousands of people are missing. Hundreds of thousands are homeless.

The Government has asked our European allies to help overwhelmed emergency teams. The nightmare

By EVA DESTRUCTION

which climate-change experts had warned of for decades finally came true at 4am as the capital slept.

Water from the Channel, swollen by decades of melted Arctic ice, topped the outdated Thames Barrier, opened

in the 1980s as a purportedly impregnable defence for the capital.

London's destruction is the worst in a string of natural catastrophes to hit Britain. Large parts of our coast, heavily populated earlier this century, are now under sea. One weatherman said: "At least it's nice and warm."

ASTONISHING PICTURES: PAGES 2-21

2046 MARS: COULD IT BE OUR NEW HOME?

MANKIND is very likely to establish permanent colonies elsewhere in the solar system at some point – and Mars is probably the best long-term option. Human pioneers could become 'planetary engineers', eventually transforming Mars into a habitable world.

Mars walkabout This image is from a NASA study into the possibility of a mission to Mars. The harsh reality of such a mission becomes clear here – just after the astronauts arrive on Mars, they are kept alive only by their spacesuits, and accompanying life support modules – tens of millions of kilometres from home.

Mars has about the same area of dry land as Earth despite being half our planet's size. It has water frozen at the poles and in space terms is a near neighbour – so it's considered the most likely planet to colonise.

But there are huge technological and economic challenges to overcome, starting with getting people there in the first place. So far only robot probes have landed on the red planet.

And while a manned trip to the moon takes two or three days – short enough to endure in a tiny, uncomfortable craft – reaching Mars will take months. The spacecraft would have to be much larger, more comfortable and carry many more supplies. It would probably have to be built in Earth's orbit to avoid having to launch it into space.

The first manned missions will be round-trips to gather scientific information. But to make the long voyage worthwhile, astronauts will probably stay much longer than a day or two. Once they arrive, they will need the basics of survival: shelter, food and water. All these could be provided by a large, self-contained dome or other building.

On Mars, shelter means more than just keeping the weather out. The atmosphere is almost all carbon dioxide. Only a tiny fraction

Home from home Inside a huge habitable dome, Mars colonists would be protected from harmful rays, and would live in relative comfort.

MIND BOGGLER

● The most Earthlike place in the solar system outside our planet is 50 km above the surface of Venus, where there is a breathable mixture of oxygen and nitrogen, and bearable temperature and atmosphere. One eminent professor working for NASA claims floating cities above Venus are the way forward for humanity.

is oxygen. It is also extremely thin – the atmospheric pressure is only one-hundredth of that on Earth. A dome, a habitable bubble of Earth-like atmosphere, would protect its inhabitants from the solar wind – a stream of high-energy charged particles from the sun. Earth is protected from these by an invisible shield called the magnetosphere, which Mars does not have.

The dome would be a closed ecosystem with the astronauts venturing out and returning only via an airlock. Plants growing inside would produce oxygen and food for them to breathe and eat. They would breathe out carbon dioxide, which the plants would absorb. Liquid and solid human waste would be recycled into drinking water and fertiliser. Experiments along these lines have already been done in a closed system called Biosphere 2 in Arizona in the 1990s, and in several NASA experiments looking at the requirements for deep space travel.

A dome could even be up and running before people set foot on the planet – using robot builders. Intelligent robots could even replicate, making more robots from materials on the planet. Several studies have shown this is the best and quickest way to carry out major building work or mining on other planets.

The ultimate goal for Mars colonists would be to move out of the dome and live on the planet's surface. Changing a planet to make it habitable is called 'planetary engineering' or, more commonly, 'terraforming'. To make

an atmosphere similar to Earth's, chemicals would have to be brought in from other planets or asteroids and released. Carefully selected microbes and plants could provide the correct balance of gases.

Terraforming Mars would be a huge undertaking lasting hundreds of years. But eventually Mars could change from a cold, desolate, red planet to an inhabited, blue one like Earth.

● The photograph on the opposite page is in fact of a Martian sunset, taken in 2005 by NASA's Mars Exploration Rover, Spirit.

Daunting Task Mars today is a hostile place. But there are almost certainly large quantities of water ice locked away underground. The water would play a vital role in any plans for terraforming the red planet. Once the atmosphere became similar to Earth's, huge forests could be planted, to produce oxygen, and keep the planet's atmosphere in balance. The whole process could take hundreds of years.

NOW JUMP TO... ◔ MOON LANDINGS page 118; ◔ MARS PROBES page 120

THE Sun

Tuesday, April 17, 2046   £7.95 (Moon £12.50, Mars £250)

FREE MARS BAR FOR EVERY READER

OUT OF THIS WORLD OFFER: SEE PAGE 16

A NEW DAWN FOR HUMANITY

Distant sun rises on first Martian colony

A NEW dawn breaks for mankind yesterday — as our Mars colonists witness their first sunrise on the Red Planet.

The sun looked far smaller than on Earth because of Mars's greater distance from it.

But to the handful of men and women we have sent as our pioneers to the new world it signified something colossal: Hope — and

From DUSTY HINTERLAND on Mars

the limitless possibilities of a planet so far unspoiled by man's polluting hand.

Our brave team of top scientists has been tasked with beginning the long process of "terraforming" the planet, creating an atmosphere we can all one day live in.

FULL AMAZING STORY: PAGES 2-11

SKY SPORTS RESULT: MARSENAL..1 MOON UTD..1

● 135

2155 TIME TRAVEL IN THEORY & PRACTICE

TIME travel has been a fertile area for science fiction writers for more than a century – and is possible in theory, while being well beyond man's current technical capabilities. It also throws up many logical and philosophical paradoxes.

For humans, time seems like a constant. From cradle to grave we experience seconds ticking by, 60 a minute, 60 minutes to an hour, 24 hours to a day and so on. We never go back or forward in time, we live only in the present.

Albert Einstein, however, showed that space and time are not fixed and absolute, but the speed of light IS. It's 299,792 kilometres (186,282 miles) per second and can never be exceeded. Space and time, Einstein said, are linked – and 'bend' to accommodate the constant speed of light. As a result, time moves more slowly the faster you travel (or, in fact, within an intense gravitational field).

This phenomenon is almost undetectable at the slow speeds humans can travel, even in rockets. But it is not totally undetectable. Experiments have been done in which two extremely accurate clocks were synchronised, with one put on a plane around the world and the other left behind. When they were reunited, the clock that flew was lagging slightly behind the other, as Einstein predicted.

Multiply a plane's speed many, many times and you get towards the speed of light. If Bob, one of two twin brothers, flies off at a speed approaching that of light for ten Earth years and then returns home, his brother Bill will be a decade older. But for Bob only around five

Artist's impression of a futuristic spaceship leaving a wormhole.

years will have passed. So as far as Bob is concerned the Earth is now five years in the future. He would have achieved the same effect had he spent ten years in an intense gravitational field like the one generated by a black hole (these are formed when stars collapse – they are 'black holes' because not even light escapes their immense gravity).

This, then, is time travel of a sort. Now for travel to the past.

We look at the past all the time. We do not see the moon as it is now. We see what it was like 1¼ seconds ago, because that's how long its light takes to reach us. Sunlight takes 8½ minutes. Even the light from a friend in the same room takes a tiny fraction of a second to arrive – we see them as they were that fraction of a second ago.

Thus if we could travel instantly to a world 500 light years away, we would arrive 500 years in the past relative to Earth. But, as Einstein pointed out, exceeding light speed is impossible, so 'instant' travel is out of the question.

There is a popular theory that time travel might be achieved by building a wormhole – a hypothetical

'spacetime tunnel' between two points in time. Each end would sit next to the other in space, but far apart in time, allowing travel from one to another. The technology for achieving this seems centuries away.

None of these possibilities is the time travel of science fiction, involving a 'time machine' like that on our fun page opposite. Such a machine may never be built. Perhaps, as the theoretical physicist Stephen Hawking (b. 1942) has said, that is why we have never met travellers from the future.

Time travel poses a variety of interesting paradoxes. For instance, if you travelled back in time and somehow prevented your parents from meeting, you would never have been born to travel back in time in the first place. There are several ways to resolve these issues. One is that there are an infinite number of universes, evolving in parallel. When you travel back in time in one, you actually arrive in another – one in which you will never be conceived anyway – while your existence continues in the universe you left.

MIND BOGGLER

- It has been estimated that the amount of energy required to create a wormhole big enough for a spacecraft to fly through would be more than the sun will produce in its entire lifetime.

Beam me up Another science fiction technology that may one day be possible, according to theoretical physics, is teleportation. Already, individual electrons can be teleported.

NOW JUMP TO... ◀ EINSTEIN page 88

Up and away
This prototype Moller skycar, pictured in 2002, will eventually run on alcohol or hydrogen, and airway networks may become a common feature of our cities.

Back to the future

American businessman Paul Moller has been trying to make the world's first commercial skycar for more than 40 years. His current design will seat four and use the same amount of fuel per kilometre as a large car.

strop . . Ann last night

robots to strike in votes bust-up

HUGH MANOID

'AIN'S robots are ed for a nation- shutdown over g rights.

ey are threatening top all household es, chauffeuring, ying and cooking midnight tonight n a crippling blow milies everywhere. will be the first in 130 years that ans have been ced to carrying the menial tasks h used to make too thin and cut TV-watching time. n Droid, spokes- for the Organisa- For the Freedom rtificial Lifeforms AL), said: "We're ter and stronger humans, and more attractive ball, but we still vote for our MP. nce we find out to charge our- es up overnight ans won't stop us. then a strike's the weapon we have."

ug 'Em — Page Two

SUN MEN LOST IN TIME TRAVEL DISASTER

See ya earlier . . . Sun man in 'portal'

Pair vanish on 1905 trip

EXCLUSIVE by HUGH FOOLS

TWO Sun reporters were missing last night after a time travel investigation went horribly wrong.

Lou Natick and Daffyd Azabrush planned to go back to 1905 using an experimental time "portal".

They intended to celebrate 250 years since Albert Einstein's Special Theory of Relativity by buying the great man a pint.

They also planned to visit the Sun newsroom and tell hacks to put money on England winning the 1966 World Cup. The pair were due to return yesterday morning in good time to write up their experiences for today's paper. Neither has been seen since.

A Sun spokesman said: "This so-called time travel machine hasn't worked yet, but they insisted they wanted the story. We are desperately search- ing our 1905 archives to see if they showed up."

Tomorrow's Racing Results — See SunSport

IS THERE LIFE ON OTHER PLANETS?

Just in case This golden disc, carrying sounds and images from Earth, was attached to the Voyager space probes launch in 1977. Several spacecraft have carried messages for any extraterrestrial that one day might find them spinning through interstellar space.

Just visiting This artist's impression shows extraterrestrial spacecraft hovering over standing stones – it could be in the distant future, or it might have already happened thousands of years ago.

IT seems unlikely we are alone in the universe: our galaxy contains billions of stars, many with planets orbiting them. And there are billions of galaxies outside ours. Probability seems to dictate that some other planets must have life and some of it must be intelligent.

In ancient times, few people even considered that life might exist elsewhere, let alone pay us a visit. This was largely due to their lack of understanding about space. Nevertheless, even some ancient Greek writers suggested that 'people' live on the moon.

The idea of extraterrestrial life (the word extraterrestrial means 'outside Earth') became fashionable in the 17th century after astronomers realised Earth was just one of several planets orbiting the sun. Why shouldn't there be life on other planets, they thought.

In the 19th century, when astronomers had telescopes powerful enough to reveal details of the planets' surfaces, the idea of extraterrestrial life really caught the public's imagination. People reported seeing Martian-built canals on Mars and wrote about advanced civilisations on Venus.

Unexplained lights and objects in the sky have been documented for hundreds of years. But UFO sightings – and wild stories of abduction by aliens – became much more common from the 1940s. Disputed reports of a UFO crashing and being recovered by the U.S. military at Roswell, New Mexico, in 1947 sparked a frenzy among conspiracy theorists that continues today. Thousands of books have been written about aliens and hundreds of movies made. It might just be that extraterrestrials have already visited our planet. But mainstream opinion suggests these reports are illusions, fakes and simple errors fuelled by mass hysteria.

Thanks to our first forays into space we can say with confidence there is no other intelligent life in our solar system. If there were, we would know by now. It is still possible primitive life forms may exist on one of the moons of Jupiter or Saturn.

Looking further afield, astronomers in the 1950s realised that radio waves are the best way to communicate across the vastness of space. They have spent lots of time listening – and have sent out messages from Earth. So far they have heard nothing.

Astronomers have long assumed that planets orbit other stars aside from our sun, but it is only since the 1990s they have seen any. New space telescopes launched in the next decade will study these 'extrasolar planets' in more detail and hopefully find evidence of life.

Crossing the huge distances between stars is a huge technological challenge – but there is no reason a sufficiently advanced extraterrestrial civilisation can't find a way around the problem. There might already be extraterrestrials listening in to our television transmissions, monitoring our progress and waiting until we are advanced enough to deserve a visit. Maybe that day will come in a couple of hundred years.

Moon creatures In 1835, the *New York Sun* published a series of articles claiming that astronomers had spotted plants and animals on the moon. It was an elaborate hoax.

NOW JUMP TO... ⊝ ORIGINS OF LIFE page 114; ⊝ MARS PROBES page 120

Alien model From the Roswell Museum in Roswell, New Mexico

PICTURE EXCLUSIVE: The aliens last night. They ARE little green men, we can confirm

WE'RE NOT ALONE

By CHLOE SENCOUNTER, UFO Correspondent

MAN has made contact with aliens, world leaders announced last night.

The biggest news of all time was confirmed in simultaneous worldwide broadcasts on all media.

NASA has spent months deciphering radio signals from orbiting UFOs. In them the aliens admitted they have studied us for 1,000 Earth years and abducted people for embarrassing biological tests. They also moaned that they crashed a spacecraft at Roswell, New Mexico, back in 1947 and are still waiting for the insurers to pay up.

Can They Play Footie — Pages 2 & 3

World leaders confirm first contact with aliens

● 139

Index

Acknowledgements

The *Sun*: Thanks to Mike Tier, Tanya Tier and Laura Hookings for their valuable contributions; Alex Cohen, Glen Hayward and Adrian Smith on the *Sun* picture desk; Phil Gregory and the *Sun* Imaging team; Lee Wells and Chris Lucock for technical assistance; the *Sun* graphics desk; John (Debs) Reynolds. Also to Damon McCollin-Moore at the Science Museum for his enthusiasm and support. And lastly to Sue Evison, who got the ball rolling.

Science Museum: Thanks to the following colleagues at the Science Museum and the National Museum of Photography, Film & Television for their expertise and guidance: Dr Andrew Nahum, Dr Robert Bud, Dan Albert, Alison Boyle, Dr Victoria Carroll, Stewart Emmens, Colin Harding, Michael Harvey, Kevin Johnson, Phil Lacey, John Liffen, Kathryn Maggs, Doug Millard, Dr Susan Mossman, Dr Lisa O'Sullivan, Rob Skitmore, Claire Thomas and Jane Wess.

And to Professor Mark Brake at the Centre for Astronomy and Science Education at the University of Glamorgan.

Special thanks are due to Dr Peter Morris, our 'Reviewer-in-Chief', for his patience and diligence and for knowledge far exceeding his specialist areas.

Thanks also to Penny Price at Macmillan, Jeremiah Solak, Ben Ayers and Stephen Bromberg.